Eat to Beat Fatigue

Ideas for Low-Energy Cooking

Easy healthy recipes

Compiled and collected by
Jane Harries

Edited by
Laura Wilson

In aid of

Eat to Beat Fatigue

EAT TO BEAT FATIGUE

Recipes Collected by Jane Harries
Edited by Laura Wilson
Introductory section and uncredited recipes © Jane Harries
Illustrations © Margaret Knight, Sarah Thompson & Sue Davis

Published in 2006 by
The Erskine Press
The White House, Eccles
Quidenham, Norfolk NR16 2PB

A private edition of this book was published by Jane Harries in 2002.

This edition © The Erskine Press 2006

ISBN 1 85297 092 8

British Library Cataloguing-in-Publication Data
A catalogue record of this book is available
from the British Library

Typeset by Waveney Typesetters, Wymondham, Norfolk
Printed in Great Britain by
Barkers Print & Design Limited

Acknowledgements

Thank you to everyone who sent in their ideas and recipes: Ainsley Harriott, Dr Michael Midgeley, Bernice Pasquier, Michael Barry, Montir Abdelrahman, Lesley de Boos, Jo and Von from the 'mechat' website, Joelle Marlow, Carole Bruce, Pat Dewing, Priscilla Wilson, Jennifer Leighton, Joe Davis, Helen Hagerty, Audrey Adcock, Rachel New, Claire Mundy, Zoe Williams and Andrew Porter. Also thanks to Sarah Thompson and Margaret Knight for their apt cartoons.

Thank you to my nutritionist Christianne Parker, who vetted the information on nutrition and also contributed recipes, tips on portable snacks and alternatives to wheat and dairy foods. Christianne can be contacted on 01604 677854.

Thank you to those publishers and authors whose recipes I have included:
Millet Tabouli, Polenta Pizza and Fruit Ice-creams © Barbara Cousins, 'Cooking Without', Thorsons 1997;
Fried Squid with Garlic and Chilli by Simon Hopkinson/Poons, © The Independent;
Gluten-free Bread and Banana Liquidiser Cake © Daily Bread, 'Gluten-free Recipes';
Lamb Chump Chops with Yoghurt and Mint, by Nigel Slater, 'Real Fast Food' © Penguin Books;
Quick Wholemeal Bread © Cranks Retail Ltd, Orion 1993;
Chicory & Orange Salad and Lamb Tagine © Michael Barry
Bridget's 'Raw' Dip, Soya Cheese and Fresh Ginger Tea © Bridget Bowcock, 2006
Creamy Butternut Squash Soup, Basic Pate recipe © Linda Lazarides, 'Treat Yourself with Nutritional Therapy', pub. Waterfall 2000, 2002
Organic food addresses are mostly from Dr Michael Midgeley's Overton Studios Trust website, www.ostrust.freeserve.co.uk.

I would especially like to acknowledge:
Ana Sanchez, Dick Davis and Theresa Coe for their invaluable help.
And most of all, two people: my sister Susan Davis, for being an inspir-
ing cook, lending an encouraging ear, typing, and doing great illustrations, and Laura Wilson, for her testing of recipes, typing and editing,
and her enthusiasm for nutrition, cookery and saving energy. They
have greatly added to the quality of this book.

And finally to Shirley Conran for her kind comments.

Contents

Every working person should have this book, whether or not he or she has ME.

I was a cookery editor of the Observer and I've had ME for 35 years. I am so grateful to Jane Harries for producing this book, for me and for you; it is clearly an efficient labour of love.

I immediately turned to page 13, 'Getting Set up for Low Energy Cooking'. All my favourite tips were in there – the best being Rooibos Chai teabags. The vile-sounding foods recommended by nutritionists that turn out to be quite tasty such as quinoa, are also within. I particularly appreciate the 4-step Chinese stir-fry on page 47, and the list of useful contacts which includes my favourite – The Village Bakery.

As a result of contracting ME, I have a wheat intolerance, and I'm hypoglycaemic, so I was delighted to see that almost all the recipes in this book can be adapted to be free from wheat, sugar, caffeine, alcohol or dairy products. There is also an excellent list of alternatives to wheat, dairy and sugar.

Shirley Conran

Foreword

People with fatiguing conditions don't just need lists of food they can't eat; they need positive guidance. This book provides just that, in the form of tasty, easy-to-cook healthy recipes and suggestions. I thoroughly recommend it.

I have treated many people with ME and other fatigue-related illnesses over the years I have been a nutritionist, including Jane herself, and have seen them benefit greatly from a healthy diet. I always leave my clients with recipes to encourage them in their new habits. In the same spirit, this book will give you a lot more ideas to help you to better health.

Christianne Parker, Consultant Nutritionist Dip ION Dip MESK

ONLY 200 MORE FREEZER MEALS TO MAKE AND SHE COULD LIE DOWN FOR THE REST OF THE YEAR!

Introduction

The purpose of this book

This cookbook is for anyone who wants some healthy, tasty recipes, which are easy and quick to prepare. You may be tired and lack time and energy to cook; you may have a fatiguing physical condition or a restricted diet: in all cases, I hope you enjoy using this book.

Most of the recipes included here are free of wheat, dairy and sugar, or can easily be adapted to become so. This is because many people are sensitive or even allergic to these foods, which causes or exacerbates their fatigue. Even if you are not, it's nice to have a break from time to time!

I have been experimenting with food since I developed ME 15 years ago. I went on all sorts of diets and became sceptical about any claims to the magical effects of nutrition. A second outbreak of ME meant I could not work. I started seeing a nutritionist and concocting recipes. Even though nutrition may not cure ME on its own, I do believe a good diet **that you enjoy** really can increase your energy and, if you are ill, assist your recovery. So I hope these recipes give you some ideas you can develop yourself, to better enjoy food and cooking.

What is in this book

I have firstly outlined some hints on nutrition, influenced by nutritionists such as my own, Christianne Parker from the Institute of Optimum Nutrition. She has helped me by suggesting substitutes for wheat, dairy and sugar, details of which are included.

Next comes a section on kitchen time-savers, including equipment, kitchen layout and food buying and preparation. Recipes are in subject areas such as 'Soups'. They are in alphabetical order within each subject area.

To help you ration your energy, I have graded the recipes as to 'amount of energy required'.

Level 1: very basic, for example, open packet and heat up, plus a little basic chopping. Level 1 suggestions are located in the low energy and portable food chapter, as they are ideas rather than recipes.

Level 2: pretty easy, such as one-pot meals you can prepare and leave to cook; stir fries; salads, and pasta.

Level 3: needs a bit more attention or has several stages, for example bread, polenta, pizza, cake.

In Appendix I there are suggestions for further reading. Appendix II contains contact details for sources of specialist and organic food, equipment and helpful organisations.

Action for ME

Thank you for buying this book. You will be benefiting Action for ME, a charity that supports and campaigns for more research and better care for people with ME. Royalties from the book's sales go to this charity (Registered Number 1036419).

To find out more about the charity's work, or to join to benefit from their quarterly magazine, helplines, information booklets and library-by-post service, please call 0845 123 2380, or visit the website at www.afme.org.uk .

Happy cooking!   Jane Harries

Notes on Nutrition

Healthy food creates energy in your body. Unhealthy or unsuitable food can decrease your energy. Most people know that for a healthy diet we should eat five portions of fruit and vegetables a day and cut down on sugar, other refined foods such as white flour, and saturated fat. There are however other factors in addition to this which may relate to fatigue.

Organic Food

Eating organically-produced food cuts out many artificial chemicals (pesticides, hormones, etc). For people who are very sensitive to certain foods and chemicals, this is vital. See Dr Michael Midgley's book 'A Life Worth Living' for the positive effects this can have. In the next section I have given some starting points for finding out if you react badly to some foods.

The other reason I think that eating organic food is important is to preserve what wildlife we have left, and most of all to improve soil quality, which in the long term ensures we can keep growing food. So support your local organic vegetable box scheme! The Soil Association has a list of providers (see Appendix II). Supermarkets are increasing their range of organic food all the time, too, and there are postal and web services (see Appendix II).

Food Sensitivities and Allergies

Some people become sensitive to a certain food category, which then upsets their digestive system and causes them to feel unwell and tired. This may only be temporary, eg while they are under stress or have a particular illness. Having a break from these foods assists healing, and then they can be tolerated once more.

Other people have permanent allergies; these are generally easier to spot, as they have more acute, immediate symptoms. A nut allergy, for example, can cause anaphylaxis: a violent physical reaction, potentially fatal in some cases. Food sensitivities can be much harder to identify, as the symptoms may be vaguer and more sporadic. In addition, if you are sensitive to a food you eat daily, you are less likely to notice any direct connection between your physical state and what you are eating. Food sensitivities and allergies may relate to a very wide range of foods, including some used in this book, such as soya or maize, and alternatives have to be found. I have concentrated on recipes that adapt to a wheat, dairy and sugar-free diet, as these are the foods that cause most reactions.

To find out if you are sensitive to any food group it is best to consult a qualified nutritionist, as the process of finding out which foods you react to can be complex. If this is not possible, you can carry out a kind of scientific experiment on yourself by excluding likely foods for a period, then reintroducing one food at a time and noting your reactions. Books like 'Treat Yourself with Nutritional Therapy' describe this process in detail.

Laura Wilson has had extensive experience of food testing, and suggests the following:

- There is a range of methods by which food allergies and sensitivities may be detected. It can be worthwhile asking for blood tests, although the results will not be able to determine sensitivities, only true allergies, eg foods that can cause anaphylaxis, such as peanuts.

- Keep a food diary for a while, and then try to identify any recurring foods to which you suspect you may be reacting.

- Some people prefer eliminating one food at a time, for a set period of time, and then trying a large amount of that food in one go and recording any reaction. As well as an upset stomach, reactions can also be in the form of eczema, headaches, difficulty in concentrating, mood swings, joint and muscle aches.

- Others may prefer to take out several foods at a time, in case they have multiple sensitivities. It takes a lot of discipline and clever detective work, but the results can be life-changing.

- To prevent further allergies, many adopt a rotational system, to ensure the same food group is not used two days in a row.

- Always consult a nutritionist or dietician if you are unsure what alternative foods can be eaten as it important to ensure you are getting all the vitamins and minerals you need.

NB: Some authors recommend you eliminate a food from your diet for two weeks. Laura's experience and that of others is that this is too short, and that a month to six weeks is best. This is because other processes and reactions may cloud the issue in a shorter period of time.

Stimulants

Alcohol, caffeine, sugar and chocolate usually boost your energy. Because of the way they interact with your body, however, this boost is only temporary and you can end up feeling more tired than you were originally. To avoid this vicious circle, cut down or exclude these products.

Balancing Blood Sugar

Sugar is addictive – the more you have, the more you crave it (I should know – I had a very sweet tooth!). In addition, eating a lot of sugar can over-stimulate the pancreas, which then causes a drop in blood sugar and hence fatigue and dizziness. This is called hypoglycaemia. To avoid this, cut out sugar and try to include some protein every time you eat. Eat 4-6 small meals daily rather than 3 large ones – including, say, a snack of nuts and fruit at teatime or at 'elevenses'. This may also speed up your metabolism, so you can lose weight! Try to eat carbohydrates and protein in the ratio of 2:1.

A reminder: proteins are things like meat, eggs, fish, nuts, beans, lentils and tofu; suitable carbohydrates include wholemeal bread, wholemeal pasta and brown rice. These are slow-burning 'complex' carbohydrates that will not give you the 'boom and bust' energy pattern that simple, quick-burning carbohydrates like sugar create. Potatoes are a simpler carbohydrate than these: always have them with protein to keep your blood sugar balanced.

Candida

Candida albicans is a yeast-like fungus which frequently grows in the gut and other areas. Through stress, illness, antibiotics or bad diet, this can grow too much and cause a variety of symptoms including fatigue. A strict diet, which includes cutting out sugar and dairy products, usually forms part of an anti-candida programme. Many books have been written about this, including recipe books. It is best to refer to these and if possible consult a nutritionist if you think you may have this problem, as it usually takes more than diet to resolve it. See Appendix I for books. Although the recipes in this book are not strictly anti-candida, some of them may be suitable.

General Note

These are general principles, however everyone is different and has different dietary needs. For more information on any of the topics I have mentioned, consult a qualified nutritionist and/or read books such as The Optimum Nutrition Bible (see Further Reading, Appendix I).

Alternative Foods

Here are some suggestions for alternatives to foods you may need to exclude:

Milk and cream   Soya milk, oat milk, almond milk, rice milk, goat's milk, soya cream, coconut milk (the latter for cooking only).

Cream cheese   There is a recipe for Soya 'cheese' in this book on page 90 which is a semi-set cheese useful for spreading and cooking. There is also a bought cheese, 'Tofutti' (soya-based spread – very good despite looking like putty). This does, however, contain partially hydrogenated soya oil. Partially hydrogenated fats have been linked to a higher risk of heart disease if consumed in large quantities, so I would not eat this daily; my nutritionist says it is fine for occasional use.

Butter   Non-hydrogenated margarine, olive oil, and sunflower oil.
NB: Many people can tolerate butter even though they are sensitive to milk, as butter does not contain casein.

Cheese	'Parmezano' stands in for Parmesan cheese – as good as the pregrated stuff in tubs. This has partially hydrogenated fat in it, but if it is occasionally used as a sprinkling over food it is OK, according to my nutritionist. 'Scheese' is nice if you like processed cheese. Goat's cheese and sheep's cheese (including feta) can sometimes be tolerated when cow's cheese cannot.
Wheat	Spelt flour (old-fashioned form of wheat, less gluten); rice, potato, gram (chick pea) and buckwheat flours; cornmeal. Also ground almonds for baking, and rice flakes and millet flakes as porridge (if you also can't have oats). Some people can tolerate rye flour and some cannot.
Thickeners	Potato flour is an excellent thickener – use less than wheat flour, or you end up with a gel (tip by Andrew Porter). Mix to a paste with *cold* water then add to hot liquid – not vice versa! Arrowroot and agar-agar flakes can also be used.
Pasta	Rice pasta, buckwheat pasta, corn pasta, hemp and spelt pasta.
Mayonnaise	Dairy and egg-free mayonnaise (so you can indulge guiltlessly!)
Jam	Sugar-free jam (Whole Earth, Meridian).
Sugar	'Fruisana' which is fructose, a fruit sugar which gives a more even distribution of energy than sugar/sucrose.

Fruit	Apple juice – useful as sweetener when cooking 'FOS' (Frugooligosaccharides) as a treat – expensive sweetener which is fine for anti-candida diets. It is a friendly bacteria product but don't use more than a tablespoon as it causes wind! Available from Bioforce and Higher Nature.
Milk Puddings	Soya puddings, soya yoghurts.
Yoghurt	Goat's and sheep's yoghurt, soya yoghurt, 'Yofu'.
Pesto	Vegan Pesto (free from dairy products).
Gluten	Xanthan gum powder (non corn-derived) eg from Barbara's Kitchen (see Appendix Two) – useful for bread-making.

Sources of Food

Shopping is getting easier for those avoiding certain foods. Specialist groceries and organic fruit and vegetables are becoming more freely available: Sainsbury's, Waitrose and Tesco have an excellent range. Write to them to let them know your feedback, and tell them about any items you'd like to see appearing on their shelves. Wholefood and health food shops still tend to have a wider range of these products, so you may find it quicker to use these outlets. These and other sources are listed in Appendix II. Lists of allergy-free foods are now provided by many supermarkets.

Getting Set Up for Low-Energy Cooking

Shopping Tactics

Going shopping is like a military campaign nowadays, as super-markets get bigger and bigger. I do all of mine by post and phone, at a village shop that delivers, and using various other home delivery services. But supermarkets are cheaper. Here are some tips for surviving supermarkets, shopping from home and getting meals delivered, including advice from other members of Action for ME. See Appendix II for details of the resources mentioned.

Surviving Supermarkets

Use a list so you don't get phased by the sheer range of goods on offer, or forget what you came in for.

Relax and take your time.

Use a walking stick or 'seat stick' if you have a mobility problem, so you can pause in the aisles. Apart from conserving your energy, this will also let other people know you have a disability, so it's easier to ask for help.

Some supermarkets will provide wheelchairs and wheel you round, if you ring them in advance; these are generally the larger stores, and it's best to phone first to find out what's available. Alternatively, Shopmobility will hire you a scooter in shopping areas. Practically all supermarkets will help you pack your things and load the car for you, if you ask the cashier on the spot. If you have lifting problems and haven't tried this yet, it can be a huge relief – swallow your pride!

For anyone who tires easily, and is short of funds, getting to and from shops can be a big problem. There may be subsidised services which can help you. These may include, according to locality: subsidised taxi fares; free or reduced travel on public transport; the blue badge scheme to help you park nearer the shops, and 'dial-a-ride' services. There is also some information on travel with a disability on the website 'Door-to-Door', and in Action for ME's travel leaflet (see appendix II for details).

Shop from Home

Since I first wrote this book, shopping on the internet has expanded greatly. Many supermarkets and specialist retailers offer a home delivery internet-based service. Even if you are not on the net, consider bribing someone who is to order for you, if you're stuck! Just check which chains offer delivery in your area: see Appendix II for addresses. Some stores offer free delivery at certain hours or if you spend over a certain amount.

Big supermarkets have refined their websites to make shopping online as easy as possible, for instance letting you keep a list of favourite grocery items to save time when you next order. Most people with ME who gave me feedback found these home delivery services to be a godsend and that complaints were handled well. But there are some drawbacks: for insurance reasons, not all delivery people are willing to carry bags to the kitchen for you (do ask what your supermarket's policy is on this), and on brain-fogged days, shopping online can still be confusing, especially if it's your first time.

For these reasons, you may prefer to use smaller stores that offer a more personal service, albeit sometimes at higher prices. For example I ring the village shop for a delivery, e-mail my local health food store and have an organic vegetable box delivered. You can also order by post, phone or the internet with companies like Goodness Direct who supply organic and speciality food. And stores like Waitrose, Iceland and Marks and Spencer will often let you shop in-store, then deliver your food at a time convenient to you.

Additional Shopping and Cooking Help

Thanks to Zoe Williams for help with this section. For those of you who are ill or have a disability which means that most of your energy goes on shopping, cooking and cleaning, it might be worth requesting a needs assessment from your local Social Services Department. This will help them decide whether you can have a home help (or funds to employ your own via 'Direct Payments') to make your life easier. However, each DSS branch has a different policy on allocating help for shopping and cooking, with some expecting you to have groceries delivered and/or directing you to home meals delivery services in your area. Nonetheless, if you can make a case for needing help with shopping and cooking to prevent your condition deteriorating, that can swing things in your favour.

Home meal delivery services exist across the country and can be accessed directly or via Social Services, who'll have a contract with your local providers. While these can be a lifeline, most people prefer not to rely on 'meals on wheels' in the long run. Wiltshire Farm Foods and the WRVS service Home Choice Meals are recommended by Action for ME members. See Appendix II for details.

Stock up on Staples

For restricted diets, organising to have the right food handy is key, or you will succumb to unsuitable food because it's all you have. Get a basic supply of staples both to cook and to snack on. Having certain basics in the house also means you don't have to shop so often. I now always have nuts and fruit in the house, and sometimes sugarless biscuits, and I find I don't miss other biscuits at all – which for me was most unexpected!

Below is my own list of useful staples and quick meal-makers: also see the list of alternatives to wheat etc already given.

Staples and Quick Meal-Makers

This is my own personal list, so I hope some of it is useful to you.

Apples and apple juice	for sweetening things and for snacks
Avocados	brilliant snack or meal, salad ingredient and dip
Beans	tinned, dried and baked in tins – Whole Earth do one sweetened with apple juice that tastes more like home-cooked. Moong and split peas are quickest to cook
Cheese	including Parmesan if you eat dairy, for loads of quick pasta dishes and risottos
Chicken	and turkey – stir-fries, grills, good sandwiches
Coconut	milk, for quick creamy stews/desserts, and desiccated

Coffee substitute	eg 'Bambu': if you do not take caffeine, it's nice to have a milky-type drink
Crackers	eg oatcakes, Ryvita – quick snacking
Curry paste & powder	eg Thai curry paste for good quick meals
Eggs	quick meals, baking, pancakes…
Fish	quick meals – fresh pieces, plus tins of tuna, sardines, mackerel and fishcakes or fingers
Flours	wheat, or if not, rice, spelt, buckwheat, gram
Fruit	
Garlic	
Ginger root	
Herbs	my favourites are parsley, basil and mint fresh, dried oregano, tarragon and dill. Puréed coriander in a jar is better than none
Herb teas	nearest tasting to tea is rooibosch and rooibosch chai (spice) I think. Peppermint tea is good for digestion
Hummus	non-dairy lunchtime spread/dip
Jam, sugarless	goes off quickly but useful for those sugar yearnings

Lemon juice, lemons

Lentils   only take half an hour or less to cook

Mayonnaise

Meat   so this has saturated fat – but the odd steak and bit
                 of liver are good for you in other ways and a really
                 nice quick-cooking treat. Some nutritionists say that
                 carnitine, which is in red meat, liver and dairy prod-
                 ucts, is good for alleviating fatigue and hence bene-
                 fits people with ME

Millet   fast-cooking grain, also flakes, for gluten-free cereal

Mustard

Nuts, nut butter to snack on

Oats   for porridge

Oils   olive, to cook with; safflower, with 'essential fatty
                 acids', for salads

Pasta   all sorts. Rice noodles are very quick-cooking;
                 buckwheat pasta tastes good and is less likely to
                 collapse than rice or corn; check you can tolerate
                 it first

Prawns, frozen   really useful quick basis for a meal

Quinoa   quick-cooking nutty grain, 13% protein (more than
                 most grains)

Rice	brown and risotto types
Salad bits	lettuce, tomato, cucumber, peppers, celery, spring onion, sometimes bags of mixed leaves
Seeds	useful snack, gives you essential fatty acids too
Soya products	soya sauce, tofu, soya milk with calcium, tofu (eggless) mayonnaise
Soups, tinned	especially organic eg Mr Bean, Suma
Spices	black pepper, cumin, coriander, cloves, cinnamon, turmeric, ginger, chilli powder
Sprouted things	High in vitamins, enzymes and some protein too – good in salads and stir-fries
Stock powder	eg Marigold low-salt
Tahini	for making hummus, salad dressing and dips
Vegetables	including instants like frozen peas and tinned sweetcorn and tomatoes. Onions for everything
Vinegar	balsamic is expensive but very nice in vinaigrette
Worcester sauce	
Yoghurt	dessert, soups, mayonnaise etc

Organising your Kitchen

Organising your kitchen exactly the way you want it really helps you to save energy, as I've found when I try to cook in other people's kitchens and exhaust myself!

Layout

The cooker, sink and fridge should be near each other and near the food preparation area.

Storage

Keep equipment and crockery easily accessible. Don't worry about appearances:
Have jars of things on the counter so you don't have to lift them
Hang favourite pans and utensils near the stove
Put a lid rack somewhere handy near the cooker to save fishing about
Keep a strainer near the sink
Put things where you need them. For example, you could keep hot drinks and mugs near the kettle, and glasses near the fridge.

Equipment

Everyone has their favourite bit of kitchen equipment. Obvious items are a blender and a food processor. A dishwasher, if you can afford it, saves time and effort. Others include:

- **Bread machine** for wheat-free bread.
- **Jar opener** eg from Lakeland (see Appendix II for details).
- **Easy can-opener.** Electric can-openers are good.
- **Plastic cutlery and paper plates** to avoid washing up on 'bad' days.

- **Swivel type of potato peeler** can be a lot easier.
- **Keep your knives sharpened to save energy!** (Easy knife sharpeners available from Lakeland).
- **Microplane graters** – expensive but make cheese-grating easier.
- **Pressure cookers** enable you to cook large amounts at one time; small one-person cookers are available now. Although they are heavy to lift, they cut cooking time by a huge amount.
- **Slow cooker** – very useful: you put in your ingredients in the morning, and the meal is ready by dinnertime, using as little electricity as a light bulb. Ideal for stews and soups – makes meat very tender.
- **Health grill** – halves cooking time by cooking both sides of contents simultaneously, and drains away fat.
- **Hand blender** – useful for getting lumps out of sauces, and easily blending soups. Safer than pouring hot liquids into a food mixer, and less washing up.
- **Perching stool**, or adjustable seat from Chestercare (see Appendix II) or an Occupational Therapist.
- **Chestercare** also do **lightweight peelers, bendable cutlery, a safety cooking basket strainer, kettle tippers, easy-grip knives, bottle/jar openers, and trolleys** that can be used to transport heavy items. If you have a disability, an occupational therapist may be able to supply this sort of equipment free. Look out for local catalogues eg from an ironmonger – many places stock these useful items.
- **Use lids on pans** to cook more quickly, and be able to do things like risotto without constant stirring.
- **Easy oven cleaning** with Lakeland 'Glide Off Oven Liner' (lasts five years, £9.95). Or put a paste made of washing soda crystals or bicarbonate of soda and a little water on the oven surfaces and leave overnight, before cleaning, using gloves.
- **Baking tins** can easily be lined with Lakeland's ready-made liners, made out of greaseproof paper.
- **A spatula** makes light work of cleaning out mixing bowls.

It can be expensive trying to buy new cooking utensils. Ask friends and families to club together at birthdays to buy you the bigger items. Let them know Lakeland vouchers, etc. are an ideal present! You won't regret investing in better equipment; it can save so much essential energy when you are trying to eat well.

Picnic Gear

Equipment for taking food out with you is important if you cannot eat 'normal' foods, or are hypoglycaemic and need snacks to 'tide you over.' Examples are:

- **A flask** for soup or herbal tea.
- **Plastic boxes**. Lakeland does a case that takes biscuits or oatcakes.
- **Microwaveable mug/bowl** with lid eg Lakeland 'Popins mug'.
- **Containers for homemade ready meals** that can go from freezer to microwave, eg Lakeland, takeaways, etc. Argos sells Pyrex dishes with plastic lids that can be used in this way.

Energy and Time-Saving Tactics

The key seems to be to set up a system that works for you. Kate P says, 'My partner makes up loads [of each recipe] ... then puts the leftovers in Chinese takeaway boxes ... which fit perfectly in the mini-fridge and microwave I keep near me, though you need to stir to make sure the contents are thoroughly reheated. When my partner's away I get veggie gluten-free pasties from zedz foods (see Appendix II) which can be frozen and then microwaved.'

Here are some more tips:
1. **Cook plenty.** Leftovers can go into soups, spreads, stir-fries, etc, or be frozen.

2. **Freeze some food** for low energy days. Cooked beans, soups, fish, bread and muffins all freeze well.
3. **Stock up** on emergency rations, eg tinned soup, ready meals, etc. Also have quick items and treats to raise your morale.
4. **Prepare** meals at a 'good' time of day for you, or do a mass cook on 'good days'. Three dishes can be made out of the same base eg chickpea soup, hummus and curry.
5. **If you are feeling hungry**, eat a small snack before cooking a main meal, so your blood sugar doesn't drop too low.
6. **Use teamwork.** 'My friend browns the meat, shaken in a bag with flour and seasonings, while I add the vegetables' (Bernice).

Weights and Measures

These are in metric and imperial, or in spoonfuls.

Abbreviations

tsp   teaspoon
dsp   dessertspoon
tbsp   tablespoon

2 tablespoons of flour weigh approximately one ounce.

Soups

The basis of most soups is a good stock. There are many products which are free from wheat, yeast, milk and artificial flavourings, available from the main supermarkets. As well as being low-allergy, they taste delicious. Brands to look out for are Kallo and Marigold, who both do a range of stock cubes and powders. Make up the stock according to the packet and use the quantity required in the recipe. You can of course, use your own vegetable stock made from boiled vegetables, or meat or chicken stock.

Creamy Butternut Soup

This is such a simple recipe and works well. It is from Linda Lazarides' book 'Treat Yourself! With Nutritional Therapy' (see below) which features nutritional advice as well as recipes. Linda says, 'Like carrots and orange sweet potatoes, butternut squash are rich in cancer-preventing carotenes. The best thing about this soup is that it tastes like something made with lavish amounts of cream, yet it is quite low in calories.'

Level 2   Serves 4

1 medium butternut squash
1 litre/1.75 pints/4 cups of soya milk
1 large onion, finely chopped
2 tbsp extra virgin olive oil
Freshly ground black pepper

Preheat the oven to 180C/350F/gas mark 4.
Cut the squash in half lengthways, and remove the seeds with a spoon. Lay the squash pieces cut side down on a greased baking tray and bake in the preheated oven for 30 minutes or until soft.

Meanwhile sweat the onion in the olive oil in a large, heavy-bottomed saucepan over a low heat.

When the squash is ready, peel off the outside skin, chop the flesh and add it to the pan of onions, stir and heat through then add the soya milk. Bring almost to the boil, stirring from time to time.

Using a hand blender, whizz the ingredients together until smooth and creamy. If you find the soup a little too thick, you can add some water to correct the consistency.

Reheat if necessary, stir in some freshly ground black pepper and serve immediately. I find that this soup does not need any salt, but you can add a little potassium salt if you wish.

Reprinted with permission from 'Treat Yourself with Nutritional Therapy' (ISBN 0953804631) by nutritional therapy expert Linda Lazarides. This book provides over 100 original recipes and is based on the author's successful treatment protocols. More information at www.health-diets.net.

Carrot and Butterbean Soup

Level 2   Serves 2

All you need with this is some good bread for a complete meal.

4oz/100g dried butterbeans or
   200g cooked beans
1/2 tsp dill
1 large or 2 small carrots
1/2 tsp fennel seeds (optional)
1 onion
1 parsnip (optional)

1 garlic clove
1 tbsp lemon juice
1/2 tsp tarragon
2cm/1 inch ginger root
Salt and pepper
2 tsp Marigold stock powder
Oil for frying eg olive

1 small swede	Parsley to taste
1¹/₂ pts/ 900ml water	Yoghurt to taste

Soak beans 2 hours. Cook in fresh water until tender: 1-2 hours. Alternatively open and rinse tinned beans. Peel and chop vegetables, garlic and ginger; fry them in oil in a large thick-bottomed saucepan until slightly soft. (If leaving soup unblended, chop everything more finely.) Add stock powder, water and herbs. Simmer for 20 minutes and blend if desired. Add beans and simmer another 5 minutes. Mix in a little yoghurt, and sprinkle on chopped parsley to serve.

Simple Beetroot soup

Beetroot soup is very easy to make, and cheers you up with its vivid colour

Level 1   Serves 3

1 packet pre-cooked beetroot or 4-5 small-medium beetroots
900ml/1¹/₂ pints stock or water (use stock powder or a cube, or chicken
  or mushroom stock)
Lemon juice to taste – 1tbsp or so
Yoghurt and dill to serve (optional)
Salt to taste; it doesn't need a lot

If beetroot is not pre-cooked, scrub carefully and boil till tender in enough water to cover. Do not remove the roots or the colour and flavour will leak out. Drain, cool and peel.

Roughly chop beetroot.
Add stock and lemon juice. Season to taste.
Blend, heat and serve with a swirl of yoghurt and if desired a scattering of chopped dill.

Beetroot and Coconut soup

I got this idea from a radio programme I half heard – I think it has a lot more ingredients than this, but this is very tasty on its own. The colour is amazing! Useful for non-dairy diets, and coconut, although fatty, is not 'bad' fat, as it doesn't raise cholesterol.

Level 1.5   Serves 3

1 packet pre-cooked beetroot or 4-5 small-medium beetroots
1 small tin (165ml) coconut milk
900ml/1.5 pints stock or water (use stock powder or a cube, or chicken or mushroom stock. I used half tsp Marigold stock powder).
Juice of half a lime
Half tsp dill (optional)
One pinch of salt if required (if you used a stock cube you may not need it)

If using raw beetroot, cook and peel as in the previous recipe.
Roughly chop beetroot.
Add coconut milk. Swirl the water or stock round the empty tin to use all the coconut milk. Add lime juice, a little salt, and dill if preferred. Blend. Heat up and serve.

Chicken Noodle Soup

Level 1

This is a good quick meal in a soup.

Rice or egg noodles   Cooked chicken or pork
Stock powder   Bits of seaweed
Spring onions   Parsley

Make up stock with boiling water. Pour over noodles, in a pan, (if egg noodles, cook 2-3 minutes). Add seaweed bits, if desired. Add cooked chicken or pork, finely chopped spring onion, and bring to the boil. Simmer for 10 minutes. Sprinkle chopped parsley on top to serve.

Emergency Soup

Carole Bruce sent in a variation on the above, without the chicken, 'for when one is feeling dreadful, and most food is either repellent or won't stay down'. In her recipe, just pour boiling water over other ingredients, wait 5 minutes, stir and eat.

Cullen Skink

Level 2   Serves 2-3

This is my version of a traditional Scottish recipe. To be more traditional and save more energy, omit the onion.

1 smoked undyed haddock
3 medium potatoes, peeled
^{1}/2 onion, chopped
^{1}/2 pint (300 ml) stock
2-3 tbsp yoghurt or (soya) cream

Chopped parsley
Black pepper
^{1}/2 tbsp vegetable oil
^{1}/2 pint soya milk

In a large saucepan fry onion until transparent. Set aside. Boil potatoes in stock; remove with slotted spoon and mash. Poach fish in boiling stock for 5 minutes. Remove skin from fish, add onions, milk, potato and cream/yoghurt. Simmer for 5-10 minutes. Serve with parsley and black pepper.

Minestrone Soup

Level 2   Serves 3-4

This is a good meal and can be adapted with other vegetables. Reheat only what you need, or it becomes mush!

One 14oz/400g tin red kidney or borlotti beans

3 pts/1.8 litres water or chicken stock

2 tbsp olive oil

1 large onion or leek

1 stick celery

1 large carrot

2 medium potatoes

4-5 tbsp savoy cabbage

1 tsp basil

1 tsp oregano

Parmesan cheese, Parmezano or pesto to taste

3 rashers of bacon, chopped

2 handfuls mini macaroni

3-4 cloves garlic (optional)

1 courgette

4 medium tomatoes (or 7 oz/200g 200g tin of chopped tomatoes)

2 tsp tomato puree

3 tbsp French or runner beans

1-2 bay leaves

3 tsp stock powder eg Marigold, if water used

1 tsp Worcester sauce (optional)

Salt to taste

Chopped parsley to taste

Stew bacon, chopped onion and garlic in 1 tbsp olive oil until onions turn transparent. Add diced carrot, celery, potatoes and courgette and stir for a minute. Make up stock with boiling water and add, with herbs and tomato puree. Add drained beans. Simmer 30 minutes to two hours, depending on how concentrated you like the flavour, and how much time you have to spare. Add pasta, finely chopped cabbage, chopped green beans and roughly chopped tomatoes, (peeled if possible – pour boiling water over tomatoes and leave for one minute for easy peeling). Simmer for ten minutes or until pasta is done. Season to taste. Serve with grated cheese, Parmezano or pesto and parsley sprinkled over.

Slow Cooker Soup

Level 1-2

This idea is from Rachel New, who says: "Soups in a slow cooker are nutritious and quick and just involve throwing in stock and whatever vegetables you have", for example:

Soup 1 Any of:	Soup 2 Any of:	Soup 3 Any of:
Tomatoes (tinned or fresh)	Potatoes	Pumpkin
Carrots	Parsnip	Squash
Green beans	Carrots	Sweet potato
Sweetcorn	Tomatoes (tinned or fresh)	Potatoes
Cabbage (chopped)	Onions	
Spinach	Mushrooms	
Leeks	Peppers	

Pulses and grains soaked overnight can be quickly added. If you aren't organised enough to remember to soak, tins of chick peas or red kidney beans can be used, or the quicker-cooking pulses such as moong beans or lentils.

You can either make a country soup with 'Herbes de Provence' or mixed herbs, or a spicy soup with cumin, coriander, chilli powder, and ginger.

Add a dollop of ketchup, seasoning, chicken or vegetable stock and a few drops of Worcester sauce to both types of soup to give it flavour. Mango chutney is a good addition to the spicy soup.

You can blend the soup to make it smooth to make it easier to eat. Blend for about three seconds to get a soup that is halfway between smooth and chunky!

To make it meaty, add chopped grilled sausages, or bacon. Pasta can be added about ten minutes before the end to bulk it out, and it will last for days, so more energy is saved! Pasta cooks quickly in a slow cooker, however, so check carefully so you don't overdo it. If you are reheating the soup, it might be better to cook the pasta separately each day so it doesn't get overdone.

Cook for 5-8 hours.

Salads

Adapted Caesar Salad

Level 2   Serves 2

This is a recipe which can be adapted for those who cannot eat wheat or cow's cheese. Croutons are vastly better homemade and go well with crisp lettuce and the other gooier ingredients.

1 Little Gem lettuce, cut into quarters
¹/₂ tin of anchovies
2 oz/50 g grated hard goat's cheese
   (eg goat's cheddar) or Parmesan

1 slice of toasted spelt
bread (or wholemeal)
2 tsp lemon juice
Olive oil

Make a dressing for the salad by mixing the lemon juice with 4 tsp of the oil from the anchovies (shake in a jar with the lid on to mix well). Slice the anchovies into halves. Brush the toast with olive oil and cut into cubes to make croutons. Mix the lettuce with the dressing, add the cheese and anchovies, and sprinkle with the croutons.

Variation for garlic-lovers:
Spread garlic purée (crushed cloves or from a tube) on the toast to make garlic croutons.

Chicory and Orange Salad

By Michael Barry from his book 'Salads the Crafty Way'. "The combination of slightly bitter chicory with the sweetness of oranges makes a marvellous refreshing salad. Add some cottage cheese and you have a delicious satisfying low-calorie lunch."

Level 2   Serves 2 as a main course and 4 as a side salad

4 medium-sized pieces of chicory
2 large oranges, navel or similar
55g/2oz walnuts, crushed (optional)

Dressing:
4 tbsp salad oil (not olive)   2 tbsp fresh lemon juice
1/2 tsp sugar   half tsp salt
1/2 tsp English mustard

Rinse and wipe the chicory dry. Trim off the base and slice the chicory across the grain into 5mm/quarter-inch rounds. Put these into a bowl, breaking them up slightly with your fingers to separate the rings.

Peel the oranges, removing as much of the white pith as possible. Slice them in half, then slice them across the grain into 5mm/quarter-inch slices as well. Remove any pips. Add the oranges to the chicory and mix gently together.

Put the salad oil, lemon juice, sugar, salt and mustard into a screw-top jar and shake well, or whisk all the dressing ingredients together in a bowl. Pour over the salad, toss it well and allow it to stand for the flavours to develop for 15 minutes before serving. If you are using the crushed walnuts, sprinkle them generously over the salad. They add a lovely crunch.

Coleslaw

Level 2

This is included as it is healthy, cheap and can be made in large quantities, as it lasts for a couple of days. With a food processor, it is also quick. It is a good source of vitamins (especially C), minerals and enzymes as it consists of raw vegetable.

Basics
Red or white cabbage, grated
Carrot, grated

Additions
Orange or clementine segments, chopped
Sultanas or raisins
Walnuts or other nuts, chopped
Apple, grated
Raw onion, sliced finely
Sesame, pumpkin or sunflower seeds

Dressings
For a mixture of creaminess, sweetness and sharpness, use mayonnaise with a little lemon juice or orange juice to taste. I eke this out with a spoonful of yoghurt and a teaspoon of olive oil.
Salt, or low-salt stock powder if reducing salt intake
Pepper
Mustard if liked
Using safflower or flax oil instead of olive oil adds unsaturated fatty acids (GLA)

Mix 'basics' and 'additions' in a large bowl. Mix dressing in a smaller bowl and add to large bowl, mix well.

Country Salad

Level 2   Serves 4

From 'Cooking Without' by Barbara Cousins. 'I love salads that mix cooked and raw ingredients and often vary this salad using cooked green beans, courgettes, or whatever I have.'

1lb/450g new potatoes	1 large avocado
3 eggs, hard boiled	French dressing
1/2 red pepper, sliced	1/2 yellow pepper, thinly sliced
Black pepper	12 black olives, optional
1 tbsp fresh parsley	4 spring onions, finely sliced

Cook the potatoes whole and in their skins until tender. Cool, and, if you like, peel off the skins. Cut into large chunks. Shell and quarter the hard-boiled eggs.

Steam the asparagus or beans for no longer than 5 minutes. Cool and slice into one-inch lengths. Peel and stone the avocado and cut the flesh into chunks.

Gently layer the ingredients in a serving bowl so that they look mixed, but have not been broken by tossing. Pour the French dressing over just before serving or serve separately.

This salad is delicious as it is, but you can add cubes of creamy goat's cheese or a dressing of tofu mayonnaise and/or yoghurt.

Eggplant Salad

From Bernice Pasquier.
Microwave a whole unpeeled eggplant (aubergine) on high for 10 minutes. Peel it and mash it up with lemon, cooked chopped onion and garlic, and seasoning. Beat in olive oil gradually as for mayonnaise and add whatever herbs you like. Yoghurt can also be added. This can be frozen, for later.

With tahini added, this makes the Middle Eastern dip 'Baba Ghanoush'.

Middle Eastern Salad

Level 2   Serves 2

This is a re-creation of something I ate in South Africa – a vaguely oriental vegetarian salad. Tahini goes well with brown rice and chickpeas, as does spinach.

2 handfuls of spinach	2 tsp fresh herbs, chopped
1 courgette	1 small handful of lettuce leaves
3 medium tomatoes	
1 onion, chopped	
10oz/200g cooked brown rice	*Dressing*
400g tin of chick peas	2 tbsp olive oil
1/2 tsp coriander	1 dsp tahini
1/2 tsp cumin	1 tbsp lemon juice
1 clove of garlic	Salt and pepper to taste

Chop tomatoes, and cook together with spinach leaves in a little water. Steam sliced courgettes with the garlic. Mix the rice with the drained chickpeas, chopped onion, cumin and coriander and fresh herbs. Make a dressing by shaking the lemon juice and olive oil, salt and pepper in a glass jar with the lid on. Reserve a little, and stir in the tahini to the rest. Combine dressing with the rice mixture, the spinach and tomatoes, and the courgettes and garlic.

Arrange lettuce leaves on a plate, and drizzle remaining oil/lemon dressing over. Put the rice mixture in the centre. Season to taste.

Millet Tabouli

Level 1.5   Serves 2

This is another of Barbara Cousins' gluten-free recipes in 'Cooking Without', in which millet replaces the usual bulgur wheat for a refreshing Middle Eastern salad.

3 oz/75g/½ cup whole millet   4 large tomatoes
¼ red pepper   ¼ cucumber
1 stick celery   2 tbsp French dressing
2 tbsp fresh chopped mint – essential   1 tbsp chopped parsley
1 dsp chopped chives

Cook the millet in ¾ pt/425m/½ cup of boiling water for about 18 minutes. Drain the millet and allow to cool. Skin tomatoes by pouring boiling water over them and leaving them for 2 minutes. Remove with slotted spoon and peel their skins off, then chop them finely. Finely dice the pepper, cucumber and celery.

Mix the millet, salad vegetables, herbs and French dressing together and leave to stand for a few hours to allow the flavours to mingle.

Von's Three-tin Tuna Salad

Level 1   Serves 3

This is from the 'mechat' website – www.mechat.co.uk – where there are other recipes and helpful hints.

200g tin of tuna	400g tin of butterbeans
400g tin of chickpeas	1 onion
Olive oil	Lemon juice
Optional Herbs Olives	

Strain the tins of tuna, butterbeans and chickpeas. Mix in a dish with chopped onion, olive oil, lemon juice and herbs and olives if desired. Serve with tomato, apple, and red/green/yellow peppers or any salad. Added mayonnaise is delicious.
It keeps for a few days.

Sudanese Salad

This is what my lodger Monty prepares with practically every meal – a nice variation on the simple salad. It is often eaten with Arabic beans (foules) and hot pitta or flatbread.

Serves 2-3   Level 1

2 medium tomatoes	1 medium onion, preferably red
Half a lettuce	1 tsp of lemon juice
2 tbsp sesame oil or olive oil	1 tbsp peanut butter
Salt and pepper to taste	

Chop vegetables finely. Mix lemon juice with oil and peanut butter; mix this into the vegetables, either with a spoon or with clean hands. Serve.

Patés, Spreads and Dips

Linda Lazarides' Basic Paté Mixture

This is from her book 'Treat Yourself with Nutritional Therapy' and is a useful way to avoid putting cheese as a thickener in patés. I generally use tinned beans to save time.

Linda says that "Like all pulses [butterbeans] are rich in protein, especially in the amino acid lysine, which is hard to get from other plant foods. Try to use a cold-pressed unrefined sunflower oil rather than supermarket oils, which are usually bleached and chemically treated to improve their shelf life. Unrefined oils should be as fresh as possible since they do not keep as well as chemically-treated oils."

Serves 4   Level 2

115g/4oz/half a cup dried butter beans (lima beans) [or one 400g tin of
    beans, drained – Ed.]
75ml cold-pressed, unrefined sunflower oil

Cover the beans with four times their volume in boiling water and leave to soak overnight. Drain and place in a pressure cooker over a high heat with plenty of water to cover the beans generously. Put the lid on and bring the pressure up to full steam. Cook for 6 to 10 minutes, depending on the age of the beans, then turn off the heat and immediately plunge the base of the pressure cooker into a sink of cold water. Once the pressure has reduced and you can open the lid, check that the beans are soft and tender by eating one. Do not allow the beans to become cold before you carry out the next stage.

Transfer the warm beans to a food processor. Using the S blade, process them with the oil until smooth and creamy. This may take several minutes. Scrape the sides down with a rubber spatula from time to time.

This basic mixture is flavoured by adding other ingredients either to the processor while blending, to the oil before processing it with the beans or by mashing them in thoroughly with the finished product.

Reprinted with permission from 'Treat Yourself with Nutritional Therapy' (ISBN 0953804631) by nutritional therapy expert Linda Lazarides. This book provides over 100 original recipes and is based on the author's successful treatment protocols. More information at www.health-diets.net.

Garlic, Tomato and Herb Paté

Level 2   Serves 4

A combination of two of Linda's recipes – she adds chilli or pesto. You could use dried herbs in this one, if you let the pate mature for an hour or so before use.

1 quantity of basic paté mix (see above) (can also use borlotti beans instead of butter beans)
1 tbsp tomato purée
2 tbsp chopped fresh herbs eg basil, oregano, marjoram, rosemary
1 clove garlic, crushed
1 tsp stock powder
Pinch of potassium salt or salt

Blend these all together in the processor.

Carrot and Walnut Paté

Level 2   Serves 4

My own creation with Linda's basic recipe

1 quantity of basic paté mix (see above)
1 cooked carrot   2-3 tbsp walnut butter (available from
1 tsp lemon juice   health food shops)
Potassium salt or salt

Blend together, sprinkle parsley on top when serving.

Bridget's 'Raw' Dip

This is by Bridget Bowcock, who is also planning an ME recipe book, and it's very quick and easy. 'Miso' is the Japanese paste made (like soy sauce) of fermented soya beans. It's a little like Marmite – very salty.

1 tsp crunchy peanut butter or tahini
1 tsp miso (either golden rice miso or dark bean miso or umeboshi paste, which is salty plum paste)
Juice of half a lemon
1-2 cloves crushed garlic (optional)
A pinch of chilli/cayenne pepper (optional)

Combine all the ingredients. You can adjust the consistency by adding more liquid (lemon/water) or more 'solid' (peanut butter/tahini).

Good as a dip for crudités – sticks of raw carrot, sweet pepper, cucumber or thin slices of cauliflower. Spread on oatcakes or crackers just before use, on hot plain steamed vegetables, or thin, as a salad dressing.

It will keep in a screw-top jar for several days in the fridge.

Hummus

I have included this because it is so useful! It goes well with a Greek salad, made with black olives and cubes of feta cheese. Laura and I vary the lemon juice and garlic according to taste.

14oz/400g tin chickpeas   Juice of one lemon
2-3 tbsp tahini*   1-3 peeled, sliced cloves of garlic
1/2 – 1tsp salt   Black pepper
1 tbsp oil e.g. olive oil   Paprika
Approx 2 tbsp chickpea water (from tin or cooking water)

If using dried chickpeas, soak them overnight, cook until tender (1-3 hours) and allow to cool. Place cooked or drained tinned chickpeas in a food processor. Add lemon juice, garlic, salt, pepper, tahini and oil and blend until the mixture is a thick paste. Add enough water to make the consistency smooth (it should still be firm enough to use as a spread), and any of the optional flavours you like.

Serve sprinkled with paprika. Spread on pancakes, pitta bread, brown bread or use to top baked potatoes.

*Tahini is a spread made of ground chickpeas available from all health stores. It comes as dark and light, the former being quite a rich flavour.

Risotto, Pasta, Pizza and a Pancake

Rice, corn, buckwheat, hemp and spelt* are some of the pastas now available that are gluten-free.They can be used in all the pasta recipes. They are more expensive, but are very convenient for quick meals. Take care to heed cooking times on the packet: undercooked corn pasta is chewy and indigestible, whereas over-cooked rice pasta disintegrates into a sticky mass.

Most of these pastas are best eaten the day they are cooked, and not reheated. Buckwheat has a very strong flavour, and benefits from a tangy tomato sauce.

* Spelt pasta is the closest type of pasta to whole-wheat, as spelt is an ancient version of wheat. Note that not all of those allergic/sensitive to wheat or gluten can eat it.

Autumnal Pasta

Level 2   Serves 1

I was inspired to do this by a parsnip and apple soup recipe I found, which is also delicious.

4oz/100g pasta
1small parsnip
$^1/_2$ cooking apple
$^1/_2$ onion
1 tsp sage (optional)

Salt and pepper
Cabbage – 2 tbsp chopped
Bacon – 2 rashers
Olive oil
Grated cheese to garnish
    (optional)

Cook the pasta according to instructions. Meanwhile, chop the vegetables and apple and stew them in oil until soft. Season and add sage. Grill the bacon and cut into pieces. Combine bacon and vegetables with the pasta. Serve with cheese grated over the top, if desired.

Bernice's Easy Risotto

Level 2   Serves 2

1 onion   1 clove garlic
1/2 cup rice   2 cups stock
Grated Parmesan cheese [or   Herbs
Parmezano] to taste   Olive oil/butter
1/2 tin tomatoes (preferably chopped)

Chop 1 onion and 1 clove of garlic, put in dish and microwave at high for 2 minutes. Add 1/2 cup Uncle Ben's risotto rice (or Arborio or whatever you have) and cook on high for 1 minute. Add 2 cups stock (or water and a pinch of salt) and half a tin of tomatoes, (or fresh tomatoes, peeled and chopped) and cook on high for 15 minutes. See if it is cooked; add a little liquid if necessary and cook a few minutes longer if required. Add chopped or dried herbs (parsley or basil) and a little olive oil or butter and serve with grated Parmesan cheese or Parmezano.

You can in fact put what you like in this ... your leftovers, tuna, cooked chicken or vegetables, browned sausage meat and so on. And there is no dirty saucepan to wash up afterwards!

Buckwheat Pancakes

Level 3   Serves '3-4 very polite people or 2 not so polite gannets'
(Laura Wilson)

Beloved of Americans, these are great with maple syrup, but also savoury fillings and strong-flavoured fillings suit them. We've lightened them by adding rice flour.

5oz/140g buckwheat flour	2 eggs
5oz/140g rice flour	1/2 pint/225ml milk or soya milk
1/2 tsp salt	1/2 pint/225ml water

For sweeter ones, add 1 tsp Fruisana or sugar.

Mix all ingredients until smooth and leave for half an hour in the fridge. Mix again. Heat pan with oil brushed over it until fairly hot. Add 3 tbsp batter; cook until bubbles form on the uncooked surface. Loosen round edges and when pale brown underneath, flip over. Turn heat down to moderate to cook other side.

Fillings
- Cooked spinach and goats cheese (plus tomatoes – optional)
- Spicy mince and onions
- Tinned/fresh mackerel, stewed gooseberries and a dollop of Greek yoghurt
- Smoked salmon and cream cheese or 'Tofutti' (see 'Notes on Nutrition')
- Olive paté (very salty)
- Blueberries, blackcurrants or sugarless jam and cream/soya cream

Treat Yourself with Nutritional Therapy has some good non-dairy, no-sugar dessert sauces to go with pancakes. (See Appendix I for details.)

Creamy Chicken and Tarragon Pasta

Level 2   Serves 1

Chicken and celery go together well when braised, (cooked fairly slowly) in a stew, with something creamy added in. This is a comforting recipe.

4oz/100g pasta	Juice of half a lemon
2 cloves garlic	1/2 tsp stock powder
Olive oil	Salt and pepper to taste
1 chicken breast	1 tbsp Mascarpone cheese
1 stick celery	(or Tofutti, a soya substitute)
1 small carrot	1 tbsp yoghurt (optional)
1/2 cup water	1/2 tsp tarragon

Put a pan of hot water on to boil for the pasta and add a large pinch of salt. Peel and chop the garlic. Heat the olive oil in a heavy saucepan, add garlic, chopped celery and chopped carrot. Cook over a low heat for two minutes to soften.

Cut chicken into 1 inch/2 cm cubes and add to vegetables, stirring occasionally, until chicken is white on all sides. Add a pinch of tarragon and 1/2 cup of water with stock powder, and simmer over a low heat while pasta cooks. Add lemon juice and heat until the chicken is cooked inside.

Drain and serve pasta, add the chicken and vegetables. Mix in a blob of Mascarpone (or Tofutti) and yoghurt, and add black pepper. Serve with steamed green beans, for example. Yum!

Fish, Fennel and Coconut Risotto

Level 2   Serves 2

Fish and coconut go well together – and so do prawns and fennel, (inspired by an out-of-print Josceline Dimbleby recipe), so I've combined them all here in a creamy risotto.

4oz/100g brown rice	1 tbsp oil for frying
Water (to soak rice)	60ml/ 2fl.oz white wine or sherry
¹/₂ – 1 pt/600ml stock	or 1 tbsp rice vinegar
3 tbsp desiccated coconut or	10oz/ 300g fish,
1 tin of coconut milk	eg haddock and/or prawns
1 clove garlic, crushed	2 sticks celery (optional)
1 fennel bulb	1 leek
2oz/50g mushrooms	3 tbsp soya cream (if
2 tsp stock powder eg Marigold	coconut milk not used)

Soak the rice in water for half an hour; this reduces the cooking time. Slice the fennel, mushrooms and celery and fry them, adding the crushed garlic. Add half the coconut milk, stock powder, a dash of sherry/wine, and the drained rice. Simmer slowly with a lid on your frying pan. When the rice has absorbed all the liquid (5-10 mins), add the remaining coconut milk. When the rice is almost tender, add the leek, sliced, and the fish. Cook for 5-7 minutes more and serve.

If you have no coconut milk, soak desiccated coconut with the rice, incorporate the mixture in the risotto, and then add soya cream just before serving.

NB: If your frying pan has no lid, either stir occasionally or use Bernice's microwave method (see p. 49).

Ham and Pea Pasta

Level 2   Serves 1

Dead easy and a taste of spring. You can vary this according to what you have in the larder.

4oz/100g pasta	3oz/80g peas
1 slice ham or 2 rashers bacon	3 tbsp single cream or soya cream
4-5 asparagus stalks	2 oz/50 g mushrooms
Grated Parmesan to taste	Olive oil and butter to cook with

Cook pasta in a pan of boiling water. Steam the peas above it. Chop ham, if used or fry bacon and asparagus in butter or margarine for 5 minutes or until tender; chop. Take cream out of fridge to bring to room temperature. Stew mushrooms slowly in olive oil or more butter. When pasta is ready, drain and mix with ham/bacon, asparagus, mushrooms and peas. Mix in the cream. Serve sprinkled with Parmesan cheese or Parmezano.

Mackerel Pasta

Level 2   Serves 1

For when you haven't much fresh food – a dish from larder staples.

4oz/100g pasta	¹/₂ tin chopped tomatoes
200g tin mackerel	¹/₂ tsp fennel seeds (optional)
Juice of half a lemon	Grated Parmesan, or Parmezano
¹/₂ red pepper	1 clove garlic to garnish

Cook pasta according to instructions on packet. Gently fry diced pepper and fennel seeds and add crushed garlic. Combine chopped mackerel with chopped tomatoes and lemon juice and add to the pan.

Heat through and add sauce to pasta. Serve with Parmesan or Parmezano sprinkled on the top.

Polenta Pizza

Level 3   Serves 1

A useful gluten-free recipe by nutritionist Barbara Cousins in 'Cooking Without'.

4oz/125g polenta or maize meal*   1 pt/575ml water
1 tbsp olive oil   2 tbsp tomato purée
Olive oil for dribbling on surface

Toppings to choose from:
sliced peppers, finely sliced onion, sliced tomatoes, sweetcorn kernels, artichoke hearts, sliced courgettes, black or green olives, sundried tomatoes, pine nuts, pineapple, tuna, prawns, sardines, garlic, chicken, turkey.

Mix the polenta or maize meal with ½ pt/150ml cold water in a pan (preferably a non-stick one). Add ½ pt of boiling water, mixing as you add. Bring to the boil and simmer over a low heat, stirring constantly for 5 minutes. The mixture should be thick and smooth. Beat in the olive oil. Grease a 10-12 inch pizza pan or similar-sized baking tray and spread the hot mixture over the surface, forming a pizza base.

Spread the tomato purée on top and sprinkle with oregano. Add the toppings of your choice, making sure you build up a substantial layer. Drizzle the surface with olive oil. Bake in a heated oven at 200C/400F/gas mark 6 for 30-35 minutes.

* You can use ready-made polenta, available from most supermarkets. Open the packet, cut the polenta into slices and proceed as before.

Pumpkin and Prawn Risotto

Level 2   Serves 3

You can use squash or even courgettes for this instead of pumpkin; yellow courgettes are nice. 'Norfolk Punch' is a non-alcoholic drink that tastes like mulled red wine with spices in it and is obtainable at wholefood shops.

½ lb/225g pumpkin/squash
1 leek
Stock cube or 2 tsp stock powder
1 pt/550ml hot water
Oil for frying

½ lb/225g red or brown rice
2 cloves of garlic
½ lb/225g shelled prawns
1 onion
Parsley to garnish

4 fl oz/125g Norfolk Punch (or red grape juice with a dash of lemon juice)

Soak rice in freshly-boiled water for half an hour, stirring in stock cube at the beginning until dissolved. Peel pumpkin and cut into bite-sized pieces. Stew chopped onion and garlic with pumpkin for ten minutes with 1 tbsp oil. Add all the rice; stir. Add some stock, and then the punch. Mix as you add the liquid, taking care the mixture does not stick to the pan; the liquid should be absorbed slowly, and more of it added whenever the rice looks dry. Slice the leeks and add them when the rice is nearly ready, along with the prawns. Make sure the prawns are cooked through before serving. Serve with chopped parsley on the top.

Pasta with Smoked Salmon and Greens

Level 2   Serves 1

A one-pot meal, saving on washing-up.

4oz/100g green tagliatelle
1/2 head broccoli
1/2 leek
2oz/50g smoked salmon

2 tbsp yoghurt or 1 tbsp Tofutti
1/2 tsp dill
Salt and pepper

Put tagliatelle into a pan of boiling water to cook. Put steamer on top of pan with chopped broccoli and leeks. Drain pasta, add chopped smoked salmon, yoghurt, dill and vegetables. Keep on ring one minute without heat (electric) or on a low flame (gas) to heat together. Serve, add salt and pepper to taste.

Vegetarian

Baked Tofu

Level 2   Serves 1

Tofu needs strong flavours to make it tasty, then the smooth creamy or crumbly texture can be appreciated. It's a good source of low fat protein, easily digestible. When baked it loses that rubbery texture and 'melts' nicely. This recipe is inspired by a macrobiotic cookery class I attended, which was given by Stacey Darrell.

4oz/80g tofu
1 clove garlic

1 inch/25cm root ginger
$^1/_2$ – 1 tsp tamari or soy sauce

Preheat oven to 400F/200C/gas mark 6. Grease a round cake tin or mini casserole dish.

Cut tofu into little slices $^1/_2$ inch/1 cm thick and lay slices on the dish, overlapping each other. Crush garlic and spread it over the tofu. Peel and coarsely grate ginger. Take ginger and squeeze a handful over the tofu to release its juice. Ginger lovers can also sprinkle ginger over the top. Sprinkle tamari over tofu. Bake for 20 minutes.

Try serving this with rice or noodles, and stir-fried vegetables.

Bean Stroganoff

Level 2   Serves 3-4

This is a cross between a baked bean recipe and a stew. The molasses and mustard mixture mellows the more it is cooked. Avoid this if you are on an anti-candida diet and put in 1 cooking apple and 3 tbsp apple juice (the latter as part of the stock) instead. If you cannot have dairy, try Tofutti instead of the yoghurt.

NB: Soya 'cream' and lemon juice would also taste similar but tends to curdle.

14oz/400g tin of red beans
2 tsp paprika
2 garlic cloves
1 bay leaf
1 onion
1 red or green pepper
1 tbsp olive oil
¹/₄ - ¹/₂pt/150-300ml stock, or
    water & 2 tsp stock powder

Bouquet garni (i.e. whatever herbs
    you have, tied in a bundle)
14oz/400g tin chopped tomatoes
1 tsp mustard (hot)
4 oz mushrooms
1 tsp molasses/treacle
2-3 tbsp yoghurt or sour cream
    1lb/450g potatoes
Chopped parsley to taste

If using uncooked beans, soak overnight and cook with one garlic clove and the bay leaf until tender: 2-3 hours. Fry chopped onions, paprika and other garlic clove together over a low heat, add chopped red pepper, and mushrooms, and stew gently. When soft, add tomatoes, mustard, molasses or treacle, stock and bouquet garni, and bean mixture or drained can of beans. Bring to the boil then turn heat right down and simmer for two hours, or more for a mellower flavour. Stir from time to time to prevent sticking; add more water if it gets dry. Add potatoes chopped into quarters, half an hour from serving. Stir in yoghurt or sour cream at end of cooking and serve with parsley sprinkled on top.

Chickpea Burgers

This is a useful recipe for preparing in advance and freezing until needed. The burgers are not too sticky to fry, yet they hold together, so they do not need flour, egg or breadcrumbs.

Level 2   Serves 3-4

400g/14oz tin chick peas
2 spring onions
1 clove garlic
$1/2$ tsp turmeric
Good squeeze of lemon juice
1 tbsp tahini paste
1 heaped tbsp raw cashew nuts

1 small egg
1 tsp each ground cumin and
    coriander
$1/2$ small chilli or 1 tbsp Barts
    Hot Chilli sauce (optional)
Salt and pepper

Drain and rinse chickpeas and blend to a coarse paste in a food processor with all the other ingredients.

Alternatively, mash chickpeas well with a fork or potato masher, finely chop onions, garlic, cashews and, if using it the chilli and mix together with all the other ingredients.

Shape into burgers and fry in a little oil until golden brown – 2-3 minutes on each side.

This is nice served in a roll with fresh coriander, sour cream and tomato salsa or chilli sauce – or the traditional tomato ketchup and salad.

Highland Crumble

Level 2   Serves 2-3

This dish is quick to make, and can be prepared the night before, by keeping the oat mixture in a separate container until you are ready to pop it in the oven. Frozen carrots or cauliflower can be left to defrost overnight then added, which is useful if you want to make a large amount for guests. To use the chickpea mixture on its own, gently sauté the vegetables in a pan, add chickpeas and tomatoes and seasoning, and simmer slowly for thirty minutes to an hour – then use as a sauce with cooked pasta. This recipe is by Laura Wilson.

14 oz/400g tin of chickpeas
1 clove of garlic
2 tsp stock powder eg Marigold
1 courgette
1 red pepper
1 yellow pepper
6 spring onions

Topping: 6oz/175g oats
1 tsp dried mixed herbs

14 oz/400g tin of chopped
    tomatoes
1 tsp tomato purée
1/2 tsp dried coriander
1/2 tsp cumin
1/2 tsp chilli powder
Salt and pepper

2 tbsp olive oil
1 tsp paprika

Preheat oven to 200C/375F/gas mark 5. Chop the peppers and courgettes into small pieces, and finely slice the spring onions and the garlic. Drain and rinse the chickpeas and mix with the vegetables and tinned tomatoes in a large casserole dish. Add the tomato puree, stock powder, spices and salt and pepper, and mix well.

If you're feeling energetic, simmer the mixture on the stove in a suitable dish (i.e. one that will go on the stove and in the oven) for 5-10 minutes. This shortens the oven cooking time.

Stir the oil and oats together in a bowl, adding the herbs and paprika, and a little salt and pepper, and spread over the top of the chickpea mixture. If you've already part cooked the mixture, either bake for 20-25 minutes, or microwave on high for 10-15. If you are cooking from scratch, bake for 40-50 minutes, covering with foil if it is browning too fast. Serve with mashed potato or rice.

Pitta or Ciabatta Bread with Chargrilled Vegetables and Cheese

Level 1-2

This is a flexible recipe – make as much as you need, with whatever you have to hand. Roast vegetables are very easy to make, and versatile.

Pitta or ciabatta bread
Goat's cheese
Carrots
Pesto
Few slices lettuce
Olives

Bottled artichoke hearts
Tomatoes
Peppers (red/green)
Courgettes
Avocado
Sun-dried tomatoes

Char-grill chunked vegetables (except for lettuce, avocado and olives) on a char-grill pan with a little olive oil. Alternatively, toss them in olive oil then put into a shallow roasting tin and roast for 20-30 minutes at 200C/400F/gas mark 6.

Heat the bread. Put vegetables in and smear with goat's cheese and possibly a little more olive oil, salt and pepper and/or pesto. Alternatively, serve with hummus. Add the uncooked vegetables such as lettuce leaves, sun-dried tomatoes, olives and avocado slices.

The vegetables can be served with baked potatoes if avoiding wheat. They also go well with pasta.

Quick Egg Supper

Level 1-2   Serves 1

This is an easy supper dish, inspired by a Moroccan meal I ate – hamburger with egg on top, a little mound of rice, both surrounded by home-made tomato sauce. Nigel Slater and Josceline Dimbleby both have similar egg recipes.

2 eggs	Half a tin of chopped tomatoes, or
1-2 cloves of garlic, chopped	2-3 chopped fresh ones
Half an onion, chopped	Herbs eg fresh parsley, basil
Chilli powder, fresh chilli or	Olive oil
chilli sauce	Salt, black pepper

Optional:

Half tin of chick peas, drained   Red or green pepper, chopped

Heat the olive oil to medium hot in a frying pan. Add the onion, garlic and chilli, if used, and fry slowly until the onion is transparent.

Add tomatoes, the herbs, and the peppers and chick peas, if used. Simmer five minutes. Season to taste and stir.

Break the eggs carefully onto the mixture and simmer slowly 3-4 minutes. Serve. Rice, potatoes or toast go well with this.

Scrambled Tofu, Celery and Leek

Level 2   Serves 4

This is a quick stir-fry, a little like fancy scrambled eggs in texture; it can be served on toast.

1 cake (250g) tofu
4 small/2 big leeks, chopped
3 crushed cloves garlic
1 tbsp roast sesame seeds or tahini

1 tbsp sesame oil
3 sticks celery cut thinly on slant
Tamari or soya sauce, to taste

Fry celery and garlic in sesame oil over medium heat for one minute. Add leeks; fry one more minute. Take the tofu in your hands and squeeze, then crumble over the mixture. Simmer by covering the pan and turning the heat down, for 2-3 minutes or until the celery is tender. Sprinkle over the roasted seeds or stir in the tahini, season with soya sauce or tamari, and serve.

63

Stir-fries

No book on quick easy cooking would be without this technique nowadays. Because cooking time is short, stir-frying saves energy (yours and your cooker's) and preserves vitamins and minerals in the ingredients you use.

The Chinese way has four steps:

Fry chopped onion with a little root ginger and garlic over medium heat.
Add protein (thinly sliced and possibly already marinated in flavourings) and stir vigorously over high heat for 1-2 minutes.
Remove protein, add vegetables (shredded or thinly sliced) and stir over high heat for 1-2 minutes.
Return meat, fish or tofu to pan for either another minute's frying, or add liquid if desired, eg stock, 1 tbsp sherry or 1 tsp wine vinegar, 1 tsp or so soy sauce. Thicken with a little potato flour or cornflour which has been mixed with 1 tbsp water to a paste. Cook broth for a minute, then serve.

Suggested ingredients:

Protein	*Vegetables*
Chicken	Green or red cabbage
Pork	Carrot
Fish	Bean sprouts
Prawns	Celery
Tofu (nice with prawns)	Red pepper
Beef strips	Green beans
	Oriental vegetables eg mizuna, mustard greens
	Courgettes

Pak choy, Swiss chard
Mange-tout
Broccoli
Spinach
Fennel
Bamboo shoots
Sweetcorn

Experiment with flavourings:

- Tofu can be marinated in soy sauce, more (crushed) garlic and 'five spice powder', a useful Chinese blend of spices available from supermarkets. Chillies can give an extra kick
- Rice vinegar is a useful substitute for alcohol, though go easy on it and try adding a little apple juice or fruit sugar to neutralise the sharpness
- Of course there are many authentic bought sauces eg oyster sauce, fish sauce and chilli sauce. These usually contain sugar, so avoid if necessary
- Sesame oil can be mixed with the cooking oil or added with the broth, for a little extra nutty, smoky flavour
- Pork can be prepared by adding salt, cornflour and powdered ginger – rub it into thin slices

Fish and Seafood

Bubble and Squeak Fishcakes

Level 3   Serves 1-2

2 mashed potatoes
½ a 200g/7oz tin of tuna/salmon
Salt and pepper, to taste
Oil for frying
7oz/200g breadcrumbs

1½ tsp horseradish sauce
1 dsp chopped chives
2oz/50g cooked cabbage
1 egg, beaten
2–3 tbsp/25-50g flour

Mash potatoes with horseradish, add chives and chopped cabbage. Mix fish and potato together and form into balls, with 50gms of the breadcrumbs. Season. Dip cakes in flour, then beaten egg and then breadcrumbs; gently fry in oil. Serve with tomato or horseradish sauce.

The mixture can be frozen after the egg and breadcrumb stage. Fry from frozen. If you are avoiding wheat, substitute flour with rice flour, and use millet flakes instead of breadcrumbs. For a good vegetarian version, use tofu instead of the fish.

Laura says: "This also works well if you bung everything into an oven-proof dish, and cover with breadcrumbs, or an oat/oil crumble mixture, and bake it if you can't be bothered making fish cakes. I've also tried spraying the fish cakes with oil and cooking them in the oven, which cuts down on oil used". (Oil spray available from Lakeland)

Fried Squid With Chilli And Garlic ('Squid-garlic')

Level 2   Serves 2 as a main course

This dish is by Simon Hopkinson writing in The Independent. It's actually from Poons, a Chinese restaurant just off Leicester Square, and they call it 'squid garlic'. I love squid – memories of Greek seaside food – and it's quick and cheap. This recipe is wonderful! I sometimes use a little chilli powder rather than fresh chilli, and it's still great.

400g cleaned squid (the larger the better, in this case)

3-4 tbsp potato flour (or cornflour but the result is not quite as crisp)

1 small egg white

Oil to fry the squid

A little salt and freshly ground white pepper

To finish:
50g butter

A splash of rice wine or dry sherry (if not having alcohol, try rice vinegar and a tiny bit of sugar)

1 large green chilli, chopped

2 cloves garlic, chopped

3-4 sprigs of coriander, leaves only, coarsely chopped

Slice the squid tubes lengthways, so revealing flat pieces of flesh. Using the point of a small knife, make shallow criss-cross incisions across the inside surface (that was) of the squid, at approximately ½/1cm divisions. Now cut the flesh into small rectangles, roughly 1 inch/3cm by 4cm...Place the pieces in a bowl and lightly season.

Heat the frying oil to 180C/350F. Put the egg white into a cup and stir with a fork to no more than loosen its jelly-like consistency. Add the egg white to the squid and, mixing each element together with your hands, massage the slimy white over the pieces of equally slimy squid. Sift the potato flour into a roomy bowl and, allowing only a few pieces to drop at a time, constantly turn the squid through it as more are added. Once well coated, tip into a sieve and shake off any excess. Melt the butter in a frying pan, preferably wok-shaped (ie with curved sides), and keep ready for later.

Fry the squid in the oil for no longer than 2-3 minutes, occasionally agitating so the pieces do not stick together. Once crisp, the slightest bit puffed up and slightly golden round the edges, lift them out, vigorously shake and allow to drain for a minute or so. Up the heat under the melted butter until it begins to froth. Add the chilli and garlic, stir-fry it around until just beginning to colour and then introduce the squid. Now briskly toss everything together over a fierce flame so that all the ingredients become one sizzling fry-up. Splash in the rice wine/sherry *[Ed: or if not using alcohol, rice vinegar and a minute amount of sugar]*, stir in the coriander and up-end the whole lot onto a heated serving platter. Eat at once, with a small bowl of chilli sauce on the side, for dipping.

Lemon Sole with Spinach Stuffing

Level 2   Serves 2

A simple way of cooking fish which, unlike frying or grilling, preserves the juices to keep the fish moist. A whole (gutted) fish such as mackerel or trout can be used; you can omit the water for these.

2 fillets of sole or plaice	1 medium onion
2 cloves garlic	4oz/100g mushrooms
A few spinach leaves	1 tbsp oil 1 tbsp water

Fry chopped onion, chopped garlic and chopped mushrooms in oil. Add water and a few leaves of chopped spinach. Put sole or plaice fillets on oiled foil, sandwich with spinach etc in the middle, and bake 12 minutes in an oven at 200C/400F/gas mark 6.

Mackerel in Gooseberry Sauce

Level 2   Serves 1

Mackerel goes well with a tart sauce, such as in this easy recipe.

1 fresh mackerel fillet

Gooseberry sauce:

2oz/50g gooseberries	1 onion, chopped
Juice of 1/2 lime	A little potato stock (or vegetable
New potatoes	stock if not cooking potatoes)

Start to cook potatoes. Stew gooseberries with chopped onion, lime juice and a little water from the cooking potatoes. Grill mackerel or bake in foil at 200C/400F/gas mark 6 for 5-10 minutes. Serve with gooseberry sauce and new potatoes.

Smoked Mackerel Dish

Level 2   Serves 1

2oz/50g mushrooms	1/2 tbsp olive oil, or butter
8oz/225g smoked mackerel	Pinch of tarragon
Yoghurt	1 hard-boiled egg

Gently stew mushrooms in oil or butter. Add smoked mackerel cut into chunks, then tarragon. Mix in a little yoghurt and heat the mixture. Cut the egg into rough chunks and add. Serve with boiled potatoes and green vegetables.

Meat and Poultry

Ainsley Harriott's Chorizo & Chilli Potato Sauté

Level 2   Serves 2

Ainsley has kindly donated this recipe especially for this book. I have invented an alcohol substitute for the vodka. Ainsley says: "This is my version of patatas bravas, with chorizo, which are uncooked pork sausages heavily spiced with red pepper, cumin, garlic and paprika. Using vodka in cooking is particularly trendy at the moment and the addition of chilli to this one is guaranteed to blow your mind!"

1 tbsp olive oil
2 chorizo sausages
1 heaped tsp garlic purée
   (from a tube)
2-4 tbsp chilli vodka (or ½ tsp
   chilli powder, 1tbsp rice
   vinegar and ½ tsp sugar)

450g/1lb cooked potatoes
2 tbsp tomato purée (from a tube)
1-2 tbsp chopped flat leaf parsley
Salt and freshly ground black
Pepper

Heat a frying pan and add the olive oil. Chop up the cooked potatoes and add to the pan. Cook for a few minutes until lightly golden, tossing occasionally. Slice the chorizo sausages, add to the pan and continue to sauté. Place the tomato purée and garlic purée into a bowl, season and pour in enough hot water to make a smooth sauce. Add to the pan and toss to coat. Sprinkle over the parsley and then add a good dash of chilli vodka, or substitute. If vodka used, set alight and allow the flames to die down. Sprinkle with some more parsley to serve.

Casseroles

Casseroles are very useful for saving your energy, and very versatile.

Pat's Casserole Method

Pat Dewing, my next door neighbour, was a professional caterer and cooks wonderful food. Here are her four steps to making casseroles, followed by three of her recipes.

1. Quickly brown the meat on a fairly high heat. (This means, heat in some oil until one side is brown, then turn and cook until all sides are.) This seals in the meat juices so the meat stays moist and tasty.
2. Turn the heat down to medium. Put in the flour (eg cornflour, wheat or rice flour) and cook, stirring occasionally, for one minute.
3. Add liquid to just cover the meat, and stir. Add vegetables, cubed or sliced, and flavourings (except for salt, as this would draw out juices from the meat). Bring to the boil.
4. Transfer to a casserole dish, cover, then cook in a cool oven (140C/275F/gas mark 1) for three hours. Top up with more water if dish becomes dry. Season to taste and serve.

Pork, Apple and Celery Casserole

Level 2   Serves 2

8oz/250g cubed hand of pork or pork steak
2 sliced celery sticks
2-3 cloves of garlic
1 tsp coriander (leaf or ground)
1 glass of white wine, cider or
    1-2 tbsp apple juice plus
    rice vinegar
1 tsp stock powder

1 cubed cooking apple
1 bay leaf
Salt and pepper
1 tbsp flour
1-2 tsp 1 tbsp cooking
    oil eg olive
Water to cover pork

Beef Casserole

Level 2   Serves 2

8oz/250g braising steak/shin of beef
1/2 pt/275 ml beer or 1 dsp red wine
vinegar and 1 tbsp red grape
    juice
2 bay leaves
1 tsp stock powder
Water to cover meat

1/2 cup cooked haricot beans
1-2 parsnips (depending
    on size)
1 onion or 3 shallots
1 tbsp cooking oil, eg olive
1 tbsp flour
Salt and pepper

Chicken, Ham and Apricot Casserole

The method here is slightly different – a quicker one to cook.

Level 2   Serves 1

1 chicken breast
1 handful of dried apricots
1 slice of ham
2 cloves of garlic
1 tsp tarragon
2 glasses of white wine, or 1 tbsp rice vinegar, or 1 dsp cider vinegar
    with 1 tbsp apple juice

1 tbsp oil
1 tbsp flour
1 tsp stock powder/cube
Salt and pepper
Water to cover

Grill or roast chicken in a hot oven (200C/400F/gas mark 6) for 20 minutes and cut into finger-sized slices. Process apricots, ham and garlic until shredded, but not a paste. Heat oil in saucepan to moderate heat and stir in the shredded mixture for 2 minutes. Add flour and stir. Add liquids; stir. Add chicken and tarragon. Bring to the boil, then transfer to a warmed casserole dish and cook in a moderate oven (180C/350F/gas mark 4) for 1 hour.

Alternatively do all the cooking in a stove-proof casserole, but take care the flour does not stick.

Here are two of Von's casserole recipes, which also appear on the 'mechat' website (www.mechat.co.uk)

Von's Lemon Pork

Level 1.5   Serves 2

4 pork chops
1 onion
Juice of ¹/₂ a lemon

Chopped fresh sage to taste,
    eg 2-3 tsp
1 apple

Optional vegetables: celery or frozen peas

Trim fat and put chops in a lidded casserole dish with sage and lemon juice. Add quartered apple (with core removed), onion and any of optional vegetables as desired. Put lid on and cook in medium oven (180C/350F/gas mark 4) for 45 minutes. Serve with baked potato or rice.

Variation: **Garlic'n'Thyme Pork:** Add garlic and chopped thyme to chops and vegetables and cook for 45 minutes. The combination of garlic and thyme changes the taste of both – mmm! Serve with roll and tomato.

Von's Lemon Chicken

Level 1

Frozen chicken pieces

Lemon juice

Optional: garlic, thyme, honey, olive oil

Thaw frozen chicken pieces overnight in lidded casserole dish with lemon juice.

If desired add any of the optional flavourings and cook in medium oven (180C/350F/gas mark 4) for 45 minutes. Serve with baked potato or rice and vegetables or salad. The dish will be black with caramelised honey, but leave it to soak and it comes off easily.

Variation: **Devilled chicken version**
As above, but add some Worcester sauce, Tabasco, or a little Chicken Tonight paste – there are lots of flavours.

Chicken, Lentil and Lemon Stew

Level 2   Serves 2

1 chicken breast
1 onion, chopped
Juice of 1 lemon, and a curl of rind
2 carrots, chopped
4oz/100g orange lentils

1 dsp oil
1/2 pt/300ml water or stock,
    and another cup later
8oz/200g potatoes
Salt and pepper to taste

Stew the chopped onion in oil until transparent. Add carrots and washed lentils. Stir for a minute. Add half a pint of water or stock and simmer for 20 minutes. Put the chicken breast in the pan with a bit more water, a big curl of lemon rind and the juice of a whole lemon. Add potatoes and simmer until cooked.

The lentil mixture on its own is very nice as a dip, or served with brown rice and fresh tomatoes.

Kidneys in Chilli Sauce

Level 1

Kidneys are quick and easy to cook and full of vitamins and good quality protein. Make sure you cut out the white and tubular parts with scissors before you start to cook, to avoid any bitter taste.

Meridian or other good chilli/tomato cooking sauce
Kidneys
Pasta or rice

Prepare kidneys as above and slice into chunks.
Cook some pasta/rice in water.
Put sauce in a saucepan and add kidney pieces. Bring to the boil and simmer until kidneys are cooked but still tender – 5-7 mins.

Lamb Chump Chops with Yoghurt and Mint

Level 2   Serves 2

This is from Nigel Slater's 'Real Fast Food' which I recommend for quick scrumptious cooking. This recipe transformed how I think of lamb!

4 small chump chops, about
   2cm/0.75 inch thick, weighing
   400g in total
6 tbsp thick, natural plain yoghurt
2 plump cloves of garlic, peeled
A small handful of fresh mint leaves

1/4 tsp each salt and freshly
   ground black pepper
1/2 tsp cayenne pepper
1 tsp ground coriander
1 tsp ground cumin

Mix all the ingredients except the lamb in the blender or by hand. Heat the grill to very hot.

Slather the spiced yoghurt over both sides of the lamb and grill until firm and ever so slightly charred at the edges. The lamb should be pink in the middle, about 4 minutes on each side.

The spice paste for this recipe can also be applied to cubed lamb to be grilled and stuffed into pitta bread. It makes a spicy sauce as well for smothering on baked or Grilled Potatoes. ('Grilled Potatoes' is another Nigel Slater recipe consisting of sliced, par-boiled potatoes, with oil and crushed garlic poured over them and then grilled.)

Lamb Tagine

This very simple yet tasty recipe is from Michael Barry's book 'Michael Barry's Waitrose Recipes'. Michael is famous both for helping found Classic FM and for his recipes on BBC's The Food Programme.

Michael says this is: "A Moroccan version of a lamb and fruit stew that's popular all along the North African coast and the Middle East. For the lentils, you can use red or yellow lentils, or the slightly larger Channa dal."

Serves 4-6   Level 2

2 tbsp olive oil	750g-1kg/1lb 10oz-2lb 4oz lamb
450g/1lb onions, chopped	cut into 2.5cm/1 inch cubes
1 clove of garlic, chopped	eg neck of lamb
55g/2oz red or yellow lentils	1 tsp ginger
1 tsp coriander	1/2 tsp cinnamon
A pinch of salt	115g/4oz dried apricots
2 tbsp browned slivered almonds	

Heat the oil in a large flameproof casserole, and brown the lamb. Add the onions, garlic and lentils and stir. Add the spices and salt and cook for 1 minute before adding enough water to just cover the lamb pieces.

77

Add the apricots, cover the pan and cook for 1 hour on a low heat. The lentils and apricots will absorb the water and thicken the stew.

Serve with spinach on a bed of pilau rice or cous cous, and sprinkle with the almonds just before serving.

Liver and Onions

Level 1.5   Serves 2

Liver, like kidney, is cheap, nutritious and easy to cook. It is rich in B vitamins – either cooking it quickly or if cooking in liquid, using the liquid as gravy best preserves these. It also contains very good quality protein.

1 medium onion	Water or stock
1 dsp oil	Salt and pepper
250g liver, in 1cm-thick slices	

Slowly fry chopped onion in oil for five minutes or until transparent. Remove from pan and keep warm. Increase heat in pan and add liver (add a little more oil if dry) and brown it 1-2 minutes on each side. Reduce heat and cook 5 minutes longer or until still slightly pink inside, not tough. Remove from pan and add to the onion.

Make gravy by adding half a cup of water to the juices in the pan and stirring over heat. Add salt and pepper to taste and pour over the liver and onions.

Variations:
Add basil to the gravy.
Add bacon – fry before the liver, or grill.
Thicken the gravy by dipping liver strips in flour before frying.

Mog's Lamb Burgers

Level 1

This is from Mog's recipes on the website www.mechat.co.uk.

If you like burgers, they are good with minced lamb. You only need to add salt and pepper, mould into a ball, flatten up and grill. They are good on pitta bread with a bit of salad. They don't need anything to bind them together because of the high fat content (only disadvantage). I usually put some foil underneath in the grillpan to catch fat and save washing-up.

Spicy Coconut Chicken

Level 2   Serves 2

Coconut milk is a delicious creamy alternative to milk, and is fantastic in sauces. It also contains anti-candida substances so is good for those on anti-candida diets. Try it in this savoury curry dish – increase the chilli if you like more heat. Creamed coconut can be used: follow instructions on the packet to make up the volume required. This dish also works well with chickpeas.
A recipe from Laura Wilson and Joelle Marlow.

2 skinless chicken breasts	1 tsp turmeric
1 tbsp sunflower oil	1/2 tsp ginger
1 onion	1/2 tsp chilli
2 garlic cloves	2 tsp water
7 fl oz/200ml coconut milk	Juice of 1/2 a lemon
2 tsp coriander	1/2 tsp cinnamon
1 tsp cumin	1/2 tsp salt

Chop onion. Slice garlic, and fry gently in oil, adding all the spices after one minute. Remove everything from the pan and set aside. Cut chicken into small pieces and brown on all sides. Add the onion mixture, water and lemon juice; simmer for fifteen minutes, adding a little more water if needed, but don't make mixture too liquid. Pour in coconut milk, add salt, and cook for a further five minutes. Serve with brown basmati rice.

Desserts and Baking

Baked Bananas

Level 1

Per person:
1 banana
1 tbsp orange juice

a few peelings of orange and
lemon zest (ie outer part of rind)

Split banana lengthways. Put on a square of foil longer than banana. Add juice and zest. Seal up and bake in a moderate oven or on a barbecue for 15-20 minutes until soft. Nice with yoghurt or cream.

Banana Liquidizer Cake

Level 3

This is from Daily Bread's gluten-free recipes (see Appendix 2 for contact details). Laura says: "This is a fantastic cake – light, moist and delicious; you could get away with less sugar, perhaps. Although this can be made in a liquidizer, it was far easier to get the mixture out afterwards when using a food processor."

1 ripe banana
2 oz/50g sunflower margarine
1 large egg
1 oz/25g ground almonds
1/2 tsp bicarbonate of soda

1 oz/25g rice flour
3 oz/75g potato flour
3oz/75g demerara sugar
1 tsp wheat-free baking powder
1/2 tsp of real vanilla extract

Heat oven to 180C/350F/gas mark 4. Into liquidizer put banana, margarine, egg, sugar and vanilla. Liquidize first then add dry ingredients and liquidize again until smooth. Turn into greased and lined loaf tin. Bake for 30 minutes. Cool on wire rack.

The following two recipes were sent to me by Priscilla Wilson, and are from 'Cooking Without' by Barbara Cousins. Priscilla says, "I really recommend the following 'ice cream' recipes [which contain] no sugar and no dairy."

Banana and Mango Ice Cream

Level 2   Serves 4 –5

The creamy taste of the banana complements the sharp sweetness of the mango. It tastes like a smoothie at the halfway stage. This would also be good with coconut milk.

3 bananas   1 large mango
140ml/5 fl oz soya milk, rice milk or almond milk (even yoghurt)

Peel and slice the bananas and freeze in a container so that the bananas are not squashed together but will separate when frozen. Peel and stone the mango and dice the flesh. Freeze in the same way as the bananas.

Pour the milk into a food processor and switch on at full power. Gradually add the banana and mango pieces through the funnel, stopping if necessary to break up the fruit if it starts to stick together. Eventually you will obtain a smooth, creamy ice cream. Serve at once or return to the freezer. If left in the freezer for long, the ice cream will set quite hard and will then need to be left out to stand for about 20 minutes before serving.

You can serve it as is or add toasted nuts, desiccated coconut or 1 tbsp carob flour. (Chopped crystallised ginger or candied peel will add sweetness.)

Variations:
Banana and Peach Ice Cream: substitute 2 peaches for the mango.
Banana and Strawberry Ice Cream: substitute 10oz/300g strawberries for the mango and allow them to thaw for 5 minutes before processing, as they are extra solid when frozen.

Strawberry and Peach Sorbet

Freeze 10 oz/300g strawberries and 2 peaches. Thaw for about 5 minutes then process along with 4 fl oz/125ml of fruit juice (apple or orange) or water.

Sugar-free Baked Apples

Level 1   Serves 1

1 cooking apple (or eating apple)
1 tsp desiccated or creamed coconut
1/2 cup water
A few sultanas, if desired

2 cloves
1-2 tsp ground almonds
1/2 tsp fructose eg Fruisana

Preheat oven to 200C/400F/gas mark 6. Core the apple – leave peel on. Score the peel in a circle round the apple 1 inch from the hole. Put apple in baking tin. Stick 2 cloves into the apple. Fill hole with ground almonds and coconut (and sultanas if used). Pour water around apple and sprinkle fructose into it. Bake for 30 minutes or until tender.

Apple corers are available from Lakeland (see Appendix II).

Bread

Laura's bread hints

- Wheat-free baking powder substitute – make with 2 parts cream of tartar to 1 part bicarbonate of soda.
- Make sure the oven is hot and mixture cool before baking.
- Fling some ice onto the bottom of the oven just before baking, to create steam; this really helps it to rise.
- Bread keeps for 2-3 days in the fridge, wrapped up well. Reheat under the grill if desired. Wheat-free bread is best toasted.
- Do leave the bread to cool first or it will crumble everywhere when you cut it! (mind you, hot bread tastes great, and if no one's looking, eat hot crumbly bread to heart's content!) The yeast will still be active in warm bread, however and may upset your stomach if you are susceptible.

Gluten-free Bread

Level 2

Another gluten-free recipe from Daily Bread.

6oz/175 g maize flour
1¹/₂ tsp baking powder
2oz/50g margarine
7-8 fl oz/200-225ml milk

3oz/75g rice flour
1 tsp salt
1 egg
6 inch/15cm tin

Heat oven to 200C/400F/gas mark 6. Beat egg, and mix all ingredients together. Pour into greased tin for 25 to 30 minutes. Leave to cool before cutting.

Crank's One-rise No-Knead Bread

This is from The Cranks Recipe Book: their adaptation of Doris Grant's original recipe, 'invented to help the busy housewife'.

For 2 large loaves:

3lbs/1.35 kg wholemeal flour	1 tbsp sea salt
1oz/25g fresh yeast (or dried,	1 tbsp Barbados sugar
amount as on packet)	1-1 ½ pints/0.9-1.2 litres water

For 1 loaf or 6 baps:

1lb/450g wholemeal flour	1 tsp sea salt
½ oz/15g fresh yeast (or dried,	1 tsp Barbados sugar
amount as on packet)	½-⅔ pint/300-400 ml water

Mix flour with salt (in very cold weather, warm the flour slightly, enough to take the chill off). Mix the yeast and sugar in a small bowl with ¼ pint/150ml of warm water. Leave in a warm place for 10 minutes or so, to froth up. Pour the yeasty liquid into the flour and gradually add the rest of the water. Mix well – by hand is best. Divide the dough into two 2-pint bread tins (round cake tins may be used if necessary) which have first been greased and warmed. Put the tins in a warm place, cover with a cloth or oiled polythene, and leave for about 20 minutes to rise, or until the dough is within half an inch of the top of the tins. Bake in the oven at 200C/400F/Mark 6 for about 35-40 minutes. Allow to cool for a few minutes and turn out on to a wire tray.

For baps: Roll out the dough thickly on a lightly-floured surface and stamp out six 4-inch/100 cm rounds. Place on a baking sheet, brush lightly with milk and leave in a warm place to prove for 10-15 minutes. Bake in the oven at 200C /400F/Mark 6 for 20-25 minutes. Cool on a wire tray. Split and butter.

Breakfast

To balance your blood sugar, have some protein at breakfast. Examples of this are:

- fish cakes
- pancakes
- vegetable omelette
- rye toast with nut butter or tahini
- scrambled or poached eggs on toast or Ryvita
- oatcakes and tuna mayonnaise
- chopped nuts with your cereal

Gram Pancakes

Level 2

From Christianne Parker, nutritionist: gluten-free pancakes

4¹/₂ oz/125g gram/chickpea flour   1 tsp salt (optional)
2 beaten eggs   8 fl oz/ 265ml water

Combine flour and salt. Mix in eggs and slowly beat in the liquid until smooth. Stand in fridge for half an hour and beat again. Oil a pan or griddle; when hot add 3 tbsp batter, tilting pan to cook evenly. Cook 20-30 seconds each side. Serve with lemon juice and smoked salmon, or soya cream cheese (or both!) or grated apple or sliced banana.

Porridge

Porridge is lovely and warming with a smooth flavour. Adding chopped nuts is a good way to help balance blood sugar levels, with the mixture of carbohydrates and protein.

Rachel's Porridge

Level 2

Make the blended apple freshly, to preserve vitamins.

Porage oats   Rice milk
Optional: handful of nuts   1 apple

Make porridge with oats and rice milk. (This can be cooked in a microwave, 1-2 minutes on high). Blend the apple and pour over the porridge. Add nuts if desired.

Jane's Porridge

Level 1   Per person

Nutritionist Anne Knott recommended this to me, because on a wheat-free diet you need a different source of fibre for good digestion: the linseeds provide that. The molasses is apparently also good for your intestines, but leave out if on a sugar-free diet. You could do as the Scots do and put in a pinch of salt instead.

1¹/₂ tbsp rice flakes	1¹/₂ tbsp millet flakes
1 dsp linseeds	¹/₂ banana
1 tsp molasses or ¹/₂ tsp cinnamon	Soya milk
2 cups water	

Soak the linseeds in the water in a saucepan the night before. Add the flakes in the morning and bring to the boil. Simmer 1-2 minutes then serve with molasses stirred in and banana chopped over the top, with soya milk. A sprinkling of cinnamon can make things taste slightly sweeter if you can't have molasses.

NB Use a non-reactive pan for this, ie stainless steel. This also works well in a microwave, using a non-metal container. (5-6 minutes on Medium High setting)

Joelle's Anti-Candida Cereal

Level 1-2

Jumbo oats
Butter (unsalted), or sunflower oil
Rice Dream

Other flaked grains you fancy
Unsweetened desiccated/flaked
    coconut

Bake a big tray of grain and oat flakes in the oven, together with enough melted butter to just coat them (4oz/125g maximum). Cook gently until lightly golden brown. Add coconut and Rice Dream to serve. If not on strictest diet, try goat's milk, which is creamier (and has more protein).

IT WAS A STRETCH TO PRESS THE SWITCH, BUT BREAKFAST HAD NEVER BEEN EASIER.

Drinks

Soya 'Cheese'

Another recipe from Bridget Bowcock, for frustrated non-cheese eaters.

Put one or one and a half pints of soya milk in a saucepan and add a crushed garlic clove, 2 tbsp fresh lemon juice and 1 tsp cider vinegar.

Bring to the boil while stirring – it curdles. Strain through muslin in a sieve.
Refrigerate.

I found that the liquid makes a pleasant drink; or I expect it could be used in soups etc.

Fresh Ginger Tea

From Bridget Bowcock.

Use 1-2 oz ginger root. (Choose roots which are smooth and shiny.) Scrape off the skin, chop roughly. Bring to the boil in 1 litre of water, reduce heat and simmer for 30 minutes. Strain.*

Drink hot, sweetened with a little honey[/*fructose/barley syrup – Ed*] if desired and maybe 'sharpened up' with a little lemon juice.

This drink is much better than sachets of 'ginger tea'. Especially good if you have a cold coming, or feel chilly and miserable on a cold winter's day. Ginger is good for the digestion. It will keep for several days in the fridge.

In summer, drink cold with plain or sparkling water.

*The cooked ginger bits can be added to curries or vegetable dishes, or added with honey to fruit desserts. Good with banana, apple, yoghurt or ice-cream.

Instant Energy Smoothies

A recipe from Rachel New.

Level 1

1 melon	Bananas
Apples	Mango
Peach	Pear

A few strawberries / frozen raspberries

Blend any combination of these fruits in a blender, or in a jug with a hand blender, with a little apple juice to make into a drink.

Laura says: Also delicious if made with soya, rice or oat milk. Milk can be heated beforehand, if preferred.

Low-Energy Ideas and Portable Food

Low-energy ideas

The **baked potato** is one of the easiest meals to do when not eating wheat. You can boil or steam the potato until slightly soft, before finishing off in a hot oven to save baking time. Coat the potato with a little oil and sprinkle with salt to get a lovely crispy skin. If microwaving the potato, add a little water to a baking dish, put in potato and prick all over with a fork, coat with oil and salt and cook according to individual microwave instructions. Sweet potatoes make a welcome alternative, and are delicious baked, as well as being a good source of vitamin A.

If you are using the oven, this is a good time to pop in a baked apple, or try baking whole onions in their skins, for an unusual accompaniment to a meal.

- Toppings for potatoes include:
- Tuna or egg mayonnaise. Chopped spring onions or red peppers, sweetcorn or avocado can be added to this
- Leftover lentil stew, or chicken curry
- Vegan pesto
- Beetroot, yoghurt and dill or chives
- Avocado, prawns and mayonnaise
- Cottage cheese and chopped herbs
- Ham chopped up with avocado and mayonnaise

Lunch

Lunch often needs to be very quick. Keep a good supply of the bread you prefer, so you can easily make toast. Mr Bean is a company that produces low-allergy soups, available from health food shops: have a few cans handy for emergencies.

Ideas

- Beans on toast
- Sardines on toast (try heating up with tomatoes & garlic)
- Tofu burgers and vegetables, such as salad
- Hummus, bread and a tomato
- Good tinned soup and bread or crackers
- 'Emergency soup' (see Soups chapter)
- 'Meal in a salad' ie salad that includes protein such as eggs, nuts or meat
- Sandwich of cream cheese or Tofutti with alfalfa sprouts, mashed avocado and lemon juice. (As in American juice bars)
- Masses of spinach and cottage cheese, with crackers or bread or potato salad
- Cottage cheese and pineapple salad
- Scrambled eggs with chopped vegetables eg tomatoes and mushrooms
- Poached eggs on spinach with muffins

Supper

- Baked potatoes with various fillings (see beginning of chapter)
- Grilled fish or chicken breast marinated in lemon juice, olive oil, herbs, salt and pepper

- Roast chicken breast/piece stuffed with pesto in slits made in chicken
- Spanish omelette made with chopped pepper and tomato, and chopped cooked potatoes, if you have any
- Tuna with chopped spring onions, peppers and tomatoes, with pasta

Healthy Portable Food

Here are some ideas for wheat-, dairy- and sugar-free portable food and snacks.

Thank you to Joelle Marlow and Christianne Parker for this section.

- Oatcakes, Ryvita, rice cakes, corn cakes
- Nut butters, tahini, hummus, soya spreads, goat's cheese
- Homemade tuna, mackerel or salmon pate; made by mixing fish, dairy free mayonnaise, chopped pepper and sweetcorn
- Bean pâtés made with puréed beans and tomato purée and/or spices and herbs (see recipes p. 44). Jordan Valley does an excellent range of ready-made spreads including aubergine pâté, baba ganoush, lentil and spinach pâté, hummus and spinach and feta

- Sticks of celery and carrots
- Vermicelli rice noodles in boiling water (see Emergency Soup)
- Nuts and fruit, pumpkin and sunflower seeds
- Crudités: raw broccoli, peppers, courgettes, carrots, celery etc in sticks to dip into soya mayonnaise, yoghurt or tahini
- Cottage cheese is OK for some with a dairy sensitivity. Try it with safflower or 'Udo's Oil' dribbled over it for extra health (it also tastes nice)
- Baked potatoes with cottage cheese, which you can blend with smokes mackerel and a little lemon juice for a very nice – and cheap – pate, or fillings given at start of chapter
- Avocado pear with tuna or prawns and dairy-free mayonnaise
- Salad and chicken, tuna, fish or tofu. For tofu, stir-fry cubes with garlic, onion and tomato with vegetable stock, leave to cool and add to salad. Or use 'smoky' tofu
- Barkat and Trufree do pot snacks that just require boiling water to be added to cook them – they even come with their own spoon
- Laura's travelling lunch: Take one third of a packet of mashed potato (Mr Mash is dairy-free), one tin of tuna in oil and some tomatoes. Make up potato according to packet, season, mix in tuna, and eat with chopped tomatoes
- Freeze soup in small portions: very useful for overnight stays, as you can take over frozen and leave in fridge to defrost
- People are very grateful if you bring your own pasta, stock cubes/powder, bread and a small container of margarine with you, and can often provide the rest
- 'Easy Gluten-free Cooking' by Rita Greer has a helpful list of snack ideas, and how to cater for children
- Munchy Seeds are sesame, sunflower and pumpkin seeds ready roasted in soy sauce, which are delicious to snack on. Also useful as a gift idea!
- See 'Getting Set Up for Low-energy Cooking' chapter for ideas for carrying cases

Appendix I: Further Reading

Gluten-Free

From Amazon's 'reader recommendations' and AfME members:

- *Cooking Without* by Barbara Cousins (Harper Collins) as featured in this book. 'Very imaginative approach' to cooking without wheat and dairy
- *Easy Wheat, Milk and Egg-free Cooking* and *Easy Gluten-free Cooking*, both by Rita Greer (Thorsons, 2001)
- *The Food Watch Alternative Cookbook* by Honor J Campbell (Foulsham, 1990) 'The only one to comprehensively explore all the different alternatives to dairy and wheat, and label recipes accordingly...the focus is largely on baking.'
- *The Gluten-free Gourmet Bakes Bread* (Hagman)
- *Gluten, Wheat and Dairy-free Cookbook* (Savill) (NB One reader says this 'has a lot of chocolate in it'!)
- *Special Diet Solution* by Carol Fenster (Savory Palate)

Sugar-Free

- *Beat Candida Through Diet* by Gill Jacobs (Vermillion, 1997).
- *Cooking Without* (see above) also has sugar-free recipes including desserts.
- *Sugar-free* by Natalie Wing. Mainly desserts, useful to have to experiment with. If you belong to Action for ME it is in their library.

General Health

- *The Complete Guide to Food Allergy and Intolerance* by Brostoff and Gamlin (Bloomsbury 1998). Useful for finding out if you have food sensitivities, and then tackling them.
- *Endless Energy* by Fiona Agombar (Piatkus, 2001) Many tips on how to decrease fatigue and increase energy.
- *Kitchen Pharmacy* by Rose Elliot and Carlo de Paoli (Orion) An excellent book, giving properties of many foods and herbs and their benefits, with recipes at each section.
- *A Life Worth Living* by Dr Michael Midgeley (Overton Studios Trust). Account of how Dr Midgeley developed a programme to successfully control his chronic ME including eating solely organic food.
  Go to www.bigfoot.com/~ostrust to buy the book.
- *The Optimum Nutrition Bible* by Patrick Holford (Piatkus, 1998) Useful nutrition handbook with sections on chronic fatigue syndrome and on increasing energy.
- *The Optimum Nutrition Cookbook.* Trained nutritionists produced this, and it's nice and easy to read, with a summary of recommendations at the end of each chapter. Comprehensive and punchy.
- *The Self-Healing Cookbook* by Turner (Earthtones Press, 2002) A strictly macrobiotic cookbook, which can be useful for avoiding dairy and excess sugars, and gives advice on trying out foods re physical effects they have.
- *Superfoods* by Michael Van Straten and Barbara Griggs (Dorling Kindersley) A lovely big book of lots of healthy recipes, many of them simple to do, with chapters at the front recommending specific eating plans for health problems. Michael is a leading naturopath.
- *Treat Yourself! with Nutritional Therapy* by Linda Lazarides (Waterfall 2000, 2002) A handbook on using food to prevent and

treat health problems. Good general information, sections on tackling specific illnesses including ME/CFS, and many nice recipes, all of which exclude wheat, dairy, sugar and eggs.

Quick Cooking

- *30-Minute Menus*, by Anthony Worrall-Thompson (Headline, 1995). There are a lot of dairy foods in this, but also many other quick delicious recipes, and a sense of humour too.
- *Real Fast Food* by Nigel Slater (Michael Joseph, 1992) An ace book with lots of really easy ideas: super sandwiches, 12 ways with frozen prawns and many egg recipes, for example.
- Ainsley Harriott's books, eg *Ainsley Harriott's All-new Meals in Minutes* (BBC Books, 2003).

Appendix II: Useful Contacts

Organic and speciality foods

Thank you to Dr Midgeley for many of these sites (see 'other references' for details of his website)

Barrow Boar
Exotic meats eg ostrich – low in saturated fats. Also gives recipes using the meats.
Tel: 01963 440 315
www.barrowboar.co.uk

Bob's Red Mill
Hundreds of baking recipes, including gluten-free, on this US site which also sells baking ingredients.
www.bobsredmill.com

Daily Bread – local to Northampton, cheap wholefood groceries including dairy-free and gluten-free products and organic food.
Home delivery in the Northants and north Oxfordshire area. Similar stores in Manchester (0161 861 0010) and Cambridge (01223 423177).
Tel: 01604 621531 www.dailybread.co.uk

Eastbrook Farm, Shrivenham, Oxon
Organic meat, poultry and cheese, by mail, phone and Internet.
Tel: 01793 790 460
www.helenbrowningorganics.co.uk

Everfresh Natural Foods, Aylesbury
Make Sunnyvale yeast-free breads including gluten-free and also

sprouted wheat bread, which tastes slightly sweet and chewy. Also sell through health shops.
Tel: 01296 425333 email sunnyvale@aol.com

Goodness Direct
Mail order and 'e-shopping' service including organic food, special diet food, household items. Full ingredients and nutritional data given online.
Tel: 0871 871 6611
www.GoodnessDirect.co.uk

Graig Farm
Organic meats including boar, turkey; also cheese, fish and a few ready meals.
By phone, mail and Internet.
Tel: 01597 851 655
www.graigfarm.co.uk

Home Choice Meals
From the voluntary organisation WRVS, who provide a range of services in conjunction with the NHS and local authorities to people in need who might otherwise feel isolated. Provides hot or frozen meals, can provide freezers or microwaves if needed; covers special diets.
Tel. 02920 739000
www.homechoicemeals.co.uk

Iceland Shopping
Iceland do an up-to-date list of foods free from gluten, soya, egg, milk and nuts, also lists of vegetarian and vegan foods: call 01244 842 842. They have a delivery service available by phone or Internet.
Tel: 0870 242 2242
www.iceland.co.uk

Musk Sausages
Claire Mundy recommends these gluten-free sausages, which have won awards – they do mail order.
Tel: 01638 662626

Nicky's Nursery
Buy seeds for sprouting from this site (or from your wholefood shop).
www.nickys-nursery.co.uk/seeds

Organics Direct
Merged with Simply Organic, sell 2000+ products including fruit, vegetables, groceries, meat and fish. Mail order.
email: info@organicsdirect.co.uk
www.organicsdirect.co.uk

Pure Organics
This small award-winning firm distributes throughout the UK and is worth contacting. Also links to a site selling additive-free burgers, including vegetarian.
email: mail@organics.org
Tel. 01980 626263
www.organics.org (website being developed April 2005)

Sainsburys
Large range of organic and 'free from' products available by home delivery.
Tel: 0845 301 2020
www.sainsburys.co.uk

Sprout People
This US site not only sells seeds (see Nicky's Nursery for UK supplier), it has recipes and explains how to sprout the seeds.
www.sproutpeople.com

Tesco
Tesco's commitment to supplying organic products improves in leaps and bounds. Excellent delivery service, order via the Internet.
Customer Service Tel: 0800-505555
www.tesco.com

The Fresh Food Co
This company has been established for ten years and has over 4,000 lines of organic and wild harvested foods.
email: organics@freshfood.co.uk
www.freshfood.co.uk

The Village Bakery
Delicious range of wheat- or gluten-free breads and cakes, some also yeast-free. Winners of several awards. Try the Rossiski or Borodinski if normal rye breads are too heavy for your taste – superb. Do mail order.
Tel: 01768 881811
e-mail: *info@village-bakery.com*
www.village-bakery.com

Waitrose
www.waitrose.com or if you are out of range of a local Waitrose, www.ocado.com who distribute Waitrose produce, including wheat-free bread.

Wiltshire Farm Foods
Home delivery of frozen, good-quality ready meals, including for special diets.
Tel. 0800 773773 for colour brochure.
www.wiltshirefarmfoods.co.uk

Wrights

Good bread mixes – just add water, no kneading, can be used in bread machines. Some organic mixes.

Tel: 0208 344 6900

www.wrightsflour.co.uk

zedz foods

'Luxury food for specialist diets': pasties, muffins and burgers that are vegetarian, often vegan and gluten free, many without added sugar. Organic where 'feasible'.

Tel. 0691 648029

www.zedzfoods.co.uk

Other references

Action for M.E.

Action for M.E. is the largest M.E. charity in the UK. As well as offering support and information to those affected by the illness, Action for M.E. campaigns vigorously for more research and better care for patients. Members benefit from a quarterly magazine (InterAction), helplines, a postal library and information packs.
NB: ME is sometimes also known as chronic fatigue syndrome.
Tel. 0845 123 2380.
www.afme.org.uk

Related articles from InterAction include:
A tough act to swallow (advice for those with difficulty eating) issue 45; 2003; p22-23)
Community care from social services – for getting help with shopping and cooking: issue 48; p38-40 and 49, p30-32; 2004.
New: Travel Information Sheet
Includes information on subsidised private travel; public transport; free car extras and wheelchairs and scooters. The leaflet is free to members, £1 for non-members.
To request an article or an information sheet, e-mail interaction@afme.org.uk or contact Action for ME

Action Against Allergy

"A very well-informed patient support charity at the cutting edge of understanding and information about all allergies and sensitivities, including Multiple Chemical Sensitivities and ME" (Audrey Adcock, Mid Devon ME Support Group)
Tel: 020 8892 2711

Chestercare

Equipment for people with disabilities, including kitchenware and trolleys.

Sidings Road, Low Moor Estate, Kirkby-in-Ashfield, Notts, NG17JZ.

Tel: 01623 757955

www.homecraftabilityone.com

Chronic Fatigue Syndrome – Your Questions Answered
A Guide for Newly Diagnosed Patients
Frankie Campling & John Campling

An easy-to-read straight-forward guide to CFS/ME, containing information about the illness and how to cope with the symptoms; includes information about children with CFS/24pp.

The Erskine Press, The White House, Eccles, Norwich Norfolk NR16 2PB.

Price £1.50 plus a stamped (first-class) self addressed 9" x 6" envelope.

Tel: 01953 887277

Door to Door

Website with information disabled people need for all types of travel including road, rail and flying. Includes shopping needs.

www.dptac.gov.uk/door-to-door

Easy to Swallow

Website by AYME member Claire Wade (AYME = an ME organisation for young people) of recipes for people who find swallowing difficult. Includes many delicious recipes by well-known chefs such as Anthony Worrall Thompson.

May be labour-intensive. Includes useful links for bed-bound people.

www.easytoswallow.co.uk

www.fixtureferrets.co.uk is great for sourcing the best supermarket deals before you shop.

Garden Organic (formerly HDRA)
All the advice, equipment and seeds you need to grow your own organic food! Including sprouts. Charity and seed catalogue, with 10% off seeds if you are a Garden Organic member.
Tel: 024 7630 3517
www.hdra.org.uk or www.gardenorganic.org.uk

Institute of Optimum Nutrition
They have a directory of nutrition consultants for £2, and also offer consultations in London (SW15).
Tel: 0208 877 9993

Lakeland Limited
Good range of kitchen equipment and containers eg for portable and frozen food.
Tel: 015394 88100 for catalogues or visit:
www.lakelandlimited.co.uk

ME Association
A membership charity run by and for people with ME, providing information, a magazine and the ME Connect helpline.
Also funds research into the physical causes of ME.
Tel: 0870 4448233
Helpline (non-members) 0870 4441836
www.meassociation.org.uk

Mechat
For recipes, shops and other information, as well as a friendly meeting place for those with ME
www.mechat.co.uk

The Overton Trust

Most of the organic food contacts I've cited come from this site, created by
Dr Michael Midgeley, who has lived with ME for many years and has it well under control. His website and trust support people with ME/CFS and fibromyalgia.
www.ostrust.co.uk

Shopmobility

Hire out scooters to those with disabilities, at shopping centres.
Tel.: 08456 442 446
www.justmobility.co.uk/shop/

Soil Association

Sell Organic Directory for £5 listing UK-wide organic suppliers including vegetable box schemes & mail order. You can access it for free (after sign-up to their site) on this website: www.whyorganic.org
Tel: 0117 929 0661
Great Association website: www.soilassociation.org

Notes and Recipes

Notes and Recipes

Notes and Recipes

Notes and Recipes